Exploring maths

Home Book

PEARSON
Longman

Series editor: **Anita Straker**

3

Published and distributed by Pearson Education Limited, Edinburgh Gate, Harlow, Essex, CM20 2JE, England
www.longman.co.uk

First published 2008

ISBN-13 978-1-405-84412-3

Freelance Development Editor: Sue Glover

Typeset by Tech-Set, Gateshead

Printed and bound in Malaysia (CTP-PPSB)

The publisher's policy is to use paper manufactured from sustainable forests.

Picture Credits
The publisher would like to thank the following for their kind permission to reproduce their photographs:

(Key: b-bottom; c-centre; l-left; r-right; t-top)

Alamy Images: Martin Bennett 44; Big Cheese Photo LLC 96; Sally and Richard Greenhill 33; JUPITERIMAGES/Creatas 45; Photofusion Picture Library 41; Helene Rogers 106; Tom Steventon 56l; uk retail Alan King 59; Visions of America, LLC 63; **John Birdsall Social Issues Photo Library:** 87; **DK Images:** 70l; Clive Streeter 37; Philip Dowell 70r; Frank Greenaway 55br; Steve Gorton 10, 81; Ian O'Leary 38; Dave King 82; Stephen Oliver 90; **Getty Images:** Mike Powell/Allsport Concepts 58; **iStockphoto:** 40, 102; John Butterfield 32; Clayton Hansen 55bl; Richard Hobson 61; Thomas Kilpatrick 56c; Don McGillis 91; Peter Memmott 13r; Maciej Noskowski 56r; **Jupiter Unlimited:** 15; AbleStock 13l, 55tl; Creatas 60; Thinkstock 43; **MB Artists/John Manders:** 83; **Pearson Education Ltd:** 105b; Merrill Education 30; NASA 49; Prentice Hall, Inc. 71; Silver Burdett Ginn 5, 6b, 6t, 8; **PunchStock:** Stockbyte 55tr; **Rex Features:** Sipa Press 105t; **Science Photo Library Ltd:** 84; **Frank Siteman:** 89

Cover images: *Front:* **Adam Periperl**

All other images © Pearson Education

Picture Research by: Louise Edgeworth

Every effort has been made to trace the copyright holders and we apologise in advance for any unintentional omissions. We would be pleased to insert the appropriate acknowledgement in any subsequent edition of this publication.

Contents

N3.1   Properties of numbers   **1**
1   Positive and negative integers   1
2   Order of operations and brackets   2
3   Solving problems   2
4   Multiples and tests of divisibility   3
5   Factors, primes, HCF and LCM   4

A3.1   Sequences and patterns   **5**
1   Sequences and rules   5
2   Find missing terms   6
3   Sequences from patterns   6
4   Using a letter symbol   7
5   Finding a term from its position   8

N3.2   Whole numbers and decimals   **9**
1   Place value   9
2   Ordering and rounding   10
3   Mental calculations   10
4   Written calculations   11
5   Using a calculator   12
6   Problem solving   13

G3.1   Area and perimeter   **15**
1   Area and perimeter of rectangles   15
2   Irregular shapes   16
3   Surface area of cuboids   17
4   3D shapes   18

N3.3   Fractions and percentages   **19**
1   Fractions of shapes   19
2   Equivalent fractions   20
3   Changing fractions to decimals   21
4   Equivalent fractions, decimals and
     percentages   22
5   Adding and subtracting simple fractions   23
6   Fractions of whole-number quantities   24
7   Percentages of whole-number quantities   25

S3.1   Grouped data and simple statistics   **26**
1   Constructing charts and tables   26
2   Calculating statistics   27
3   Interpreting graphs and diagrams   28

G3.2   Angles   **30**
1   Measuring and drawing angles   30
2   Angles on a straight line   31
3   Angles at a point   32

S3.2   Probability 1   **33**
1   The probability scale   33
2   Equally likely outcomes   34
3   Probability experiments   34

N3.4   Decimals and measure   **35**
1   Estimating and converting measurements   35
2   Reading scales   36
3   Solving word problems   37
4   Problems involving time   38
5   Multiplication and division calculations   38
6   Solving problems with a calculator   39

A3.2   Equations and formulae   **40**
1   Terms and expressions   40
2   Multiplying terms in brackets   41
3   Formulae   41
4   Equations: addition and subtraction   42
5   Equations: multiplication and division   42

S3.3   Enquiry 1   **43**
1   Planning a project   43
2   Collecting data 1   45
3   Drawing charts and graphs using ICT   45
4   Collecting data 2   47
5   Interpreting charts and graphs   47

A3.3   Functions and graphs   **48**
1   Functions and mappings   48
2   Plotting points   49
3   Straight-line graphs   50
4   Plotting straight-line graphs   51
5   Sequences   52

G3.3	**Transformations**	**53**
1	Line symmetry	53
2	Reflections	54
3	Rotation symmetry	55
4	Rotations	56
5	Translations	57
N3.5	**Percentages, ratio and proportion**	**58**
1	Equivalent fractions and percentages	58
2	Finding percentages, including discounts	59
3	Dividing a quantity in a given ratio	60
4	Direct proportion	61
5	Conversion graphs	62
G3.4	**Properties of shapes**	**63**
1	Parallel and perpendicular lines	63
2	Properties of shapes 1	64
3	Properties of shapes 2	65
4	Investigating shapes	66
5	Angle sum of a triangle	67
6	Solving problems	68
S3.4	**Enquiry 2**	**69**
1	Collecting data	69
2	Calculating statistics	70
3	Using statistics	72
4	Representing data	73
5	Interpreting and discussing data	74
G3.5	**Constructions**	**76**
1	Drawing line segments and parallel lines	76
2	Constructing shapes with right angles	77
3	Acute, obtuse and reflex angles	77
4	Constructing triangles	79
5	Nets of 3D shapes	80
6	Properties of 3D shapes	81

A3.4	**Using algebra**	**82**
1	Working with expressions	82
2	Functions and equations	83
3	Solving equations	84
4	Square and triangular numbers	85
5	More sequences from patterns	86
6	Interpreting real-life graphs 1	87
7	Interpreting real-life graphs 2	88
8	Using ICT to draw graphs	89
S3.5	**Probability 2**	**90**
1	Equally likely outcomes	90
2	Experimental probability	91
3	Comparing probabilities	92
N3.6	**Solving number problems**	**93**
1	Word problems	93
2	Working with fractions	94
3	Fractions, decimals and percentages	95
4	Comparing proportions	96
5	Ratio and proportion problems	97
R3.1	**Revision unit 1**	**98**
1	Whole number and decimal calculations	98
2	Fractions, decimals and percentages	99
3	Expressions and equations	100
4	Charts, graphs and simple statistics	101
5	Probability	102
R3.2	**Revision unit 2**	**104**
1	Solving word problems	104
2	Ratio	105
3	Sequences, functions and graphs	107
4	Area and perimeter	108
5	Symmetry and transformations	110

Properties of numbers

TASK 1: Positive and negative integers

⦿ Points to remember

- ⊙ Numbers get less as you count back along the number line, so $-8 < -4$.
- ⊙ To add a positive number, count on along the number line.
  To add a negative number, count back along the number line.

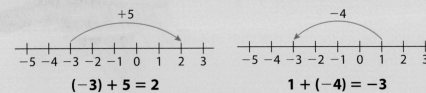

$$(-3) + 5 = 2 \qquad\qquad 1 + (-4) = -3$$

- ⊙ Adding -6 is the same as subtracting 6.
  Subtracting -6 is the same as adding 6.

---

① Work out these sums and differences.

a $6 + (-3)$	**b** $(-2) + 7$	**c** $(-3) + (-8)$
d $5 + (-9)$	**e** $(-10) + 3$	**f** $(-6) + 1 + (-5)$
g $8 - (-2)$	**h** $(-9) - 7$	**i** $(-5) - (-9)$
j $(-9) - (-5)$		

② In a magic square, each row, column and diagonal
has the same total.
In this square, the magic total is 6.
Make a 3 by 3 magic square using these numbers:
$-4, \quad -3, \quad -2, \quad -1, \quad 0, \quad 1, \quad 2, \quad 3, \quad 4$
Each row, column and diagonal must add up to 0.

3	−2	5
4	2	0
−1	6	1

TASK 2: Order of operations and brackets

Points to remember
- Work out any calculation in brackets first.
- After brackets, multiply and divide before you add and subtract.

(1) **Without using your calculator**, work out:

    a $6 + 10 \times 4$ b $16 - 8 \div 4$ c $4 \times 5 - 1$

    d $24 \div (5 - 1)$ e $(6 - 3) \times 5$ f $-3 + (12 \div 6)$

(2) Find the missing number in each of these calculations.

    a $10 - \square \times 2 = 8$ b $12 \div 3 + \square = 9$ c $\square - 20 \div 4 = 5$ d $3 \times \square - 8 = 10$

(3) In this expression, you can replace each ● with one of the operations $+, -, \times$ and $\div$.

$$6 \; \bullet \; 3 \; \bullet \; 2$$

Replace each ● to make an expression with a value of:

    a   12   b   0

TASK 3: Solving problems

Points to remember
- Work out any calculation in brackets first.
- After brackets, multiply and divide before you add and subtract.

You can make the numbers 1, 2 and 3 using the digit 4, any of the operations $+, -, \times$ and $\div$, and brackets. For example:

    $4 \div 4 = 1$ $(4 + 4) \div 4 = 2$ $4 - (4 \div 4) = 3$

Use the digit 3, any of the operations $+, -, \times$ and $\div$, and brackets.
Make the numbers 1 to 12.

  ▶   You can use the digit 3 as many times as you like each time.

  ▶   You don't need to use all four operations.

  ▶   You can repeat an operation if you want to.

  ▶   Use brackets where they are needed.

TASK 4: Multiples and tests of divisibility

Points to remember

- A **multiple** of a number divides exactly by the number.
- There are simple **tests for divisibility** by 2, 3, 4, 5, 9 and 10.
- If a number is divisible by **6**, it must be divisible by **2** and divisible by **3.**
- The **square** of a number is the number multiplied by itself.
  If the square of 9 is 81, then the **square root** of 81 is 9 ($9^2 = 81$, $\sqrt{81} = 9$).
- Square before you multiply, divide, add or subtract.

Example

You can find the value of 5^2 by pressing these calculator keys: $\boxed{5}\,\boxed{x^2}$

You usually find the square root of 81 by pressing these keys: $\boxed{\sqrt{}}\,\boxed{8}\,\boxed{1}$

On some calculators you press the square root key last like this: $\boxed{8}\,\boxed{1}\,\boxed{\sqrt{}}$

1. Choose from the numbers in the box. Write:
   a five numbers that are divisible by 3
   b four numbers that are divisible by 4
   c three numbers that are divisible by 5
   d four numbers that are multiples of 7

   > 35   60   12   15   84   42   56

2. **Use your calculator** to work out the value of each of these.
   a 24^2
   b 2.7^2
   c $\sqrt{324}$
   d $\sqrt{225}$
   e 5×8^2
   f $112 \div 4^2$
   g $(19 - 8)^2$
   h $4^2 \div 5^2$

3. Try this investigation.
   Use each of the digits 1 to 9 only once.

   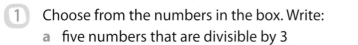

   Make different multiples of 6.
   Can you use all the digits?

TASK 5: Factors, primes, HCF and LCM

Points to remember

- The **factors** of a whole number are all the whole numbers that divide into it exactly.
- Factors occur in pairs. The factor pairs for 10 are 1 × 10 and 2 × 5.
- **Prime numbers** have only two different factors, themselves and 1. 1 is not a prime number.
- You can find the **highest common factor (HCF)** of two numbers by looking at lists of their factors.
- You can find the **lowest common multiple (LCM)** of two numbers by looking at lists of their multiples.

① Write all the factors of 56.

② Write a factor of 75 that is bigger than 20 but smaller than 30.

③ What is the highest common factor (HCF) of 32 and 48?

④ What is the lowest common multiple (LCM) of 15 and 20?

⑤ 13 is a special prime number.

When you reverse its digits the number you get is also prime.

> 13 is a prime number.
> 31 is a prime number.

Besides 13 and 31, there are seven more prime numbers between 10 and 100 that are also prime when their digits are reversed.
Find them all.

Sequences and patterns

TASK 1: Sequences and rules

> **◉ Points to remember**
>
> ⊙ A **sequence** of numbers follows a rule.
> ⊙ You can work out the next term in a sequence if you know the **term-to-term rule**.
> ⊙ If the rule is 'add 2', then the number after 15 will be 17.

① Write the rule and the next five terms for each sequence.

  a 6, 11, 16, 21, …

  b 200, 193, 186, 179, …

  c 1, 4.5, 8, 11.5, …

  d 1.05, 1.25, 1.45, 1.65, …

  e 1, 0.97, 0.94, 0.91, …

  f −1, −3, −5, −7, …

  g −100, −95, −90, −85, …

  h 3, 6, 12, 24, …

  i 1024, 512, 256, 128, …

  j 250, 227, 204, 181, …

TASK 2: Finding missing terms

⊙ Points to remember

- If the step size is always the same, and there are 3 steps between two known terms, each step is $\frac{1}{3}$ of the difference between the two terms.
- You can work out the next term in a sequence if you know the term-to-term rule.

① In these sequences, the step size is always the same.
Copy each sequence. Fill in the missing terms.

a 2, 9, …, 23, …, 37, …

b …, 45, 40, 35, …, …, …

c …, …, …, 27, 36, 45, …

d −10, −6, −2, 2, …, …, 14, …

② Copy each sequence. Fill in the missing terms.

a 2, 4, 8, …, …, …, 128, …

b 48, …, 12, 6, …, …, 0.75, …

TASK 3: Sequences from patterns

⊙ Points to remember

- You can make sequences from patterns of shapes that follow a rule.
- Work out the pattern by looking at the way it increases or decreases.

Here is a sequence of patterns made from red and blue tiles.

  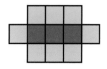

1st pattern   2nd pattern   3rd pattern

(1) The sequence continues in the same way.

    a Write the sequence for the number of red tiles.

    b Write the sequence for the number of blue tiles.

    c How many red tiles will be in the 4th pattern?

    d How many red tiles will be in the 10th pattern?

    e How many blue tiles will be in the 4th pattern?

    f How many blue tiles will be in the 10th pattern?

(2) **a** Describe how the number of red tiles increases each time.

    b Describe how the number of blue tiles increases each time.

(3) **a** How many red tiles will be in the 100th pattern?

    b How many blue tiles will be in the 100th pattern?

    c Explain how to work out the number of blue tiles in the 100th pattern.

TASK 4: Using a letter symbol

 Points to remember

⊙ The **expression** $n + 6$ is an instruction telling you to 'add the number 6 to the number n'.

When $n = 1$, $n + 6 = 7$.

1 Copy and complete this table.

	Expression	$n = 1$	$n = 2$	$n = 3$	$n = 4$	$n = 5$
a	$n + 9$					14
b	$n - 2$	-1				
c	$7n$			21		
d	$3n + 4$		10			

2 Write these instructions in words.

a $n + 3$ b $n - 7$

c $4 + n$ d $7 - n$

TASK 5: Finding a term from its position

Points to remember

⊙ You can work out any term in a sequence if you know a rule to find a term from its position.

⊙ If the formula for the **nth term** is $3n + 1$, the 9th term is $3 \times 9 + 1 = 28$.

1 Write the next five terms of each sequence using the formula for the nth term.

Formula for nth term	**Sequence**
a $8n$	8, 16, …
b $8n + 3$	11, 19, …
c $9n - 1$	8, 17, …
d $3n + 5$	8, 11, …
e $4n - 3$	1, 5, …

Whole numbers and decimals

TASK 1: Place value

 Points to remember

- $0.3 = \frac{3}{10}$ $0.09 = \frac{9}{100}$ $0.004 = \frac{4}{1000}$
- When a whole number or decimal is:
  - multiplied by 10, its digits move 1 place to the left;
  - multiplied by 100, its digits move 2 places to the left;
  - multiplied by 1000, its digits move 3 places to the left.
- When a whole number or decimal is:
  - divided by 10, the digits move 1 place to the right;
  - divided by 100, the digits move 2 places to the right;
  - divided by 1000, the digits move 3 places to the right.

1. Write these as fractions.

   a 0.9   b 0.07   c 0.003

   d 0.17   e 0.651   f 3.59

2. Write these as decimals.

   a $\frac{7}{10}$ b $\frac{3}{100}$ c $\frac{8}{1000}$

   d $\frac{75}{100}$ e $\frac{82}{1000}$ f $\frac{463}{1000}$

3. Copy and complete these calculations.

   a $0.7 \times 100 =$ b $13.8 \div 100 =$ c $0.02 \times 1000 =$

   d $3002 \div 1000 =$ e $0.05 \times 10 =$ f $0.035 \div 10 =$

TASK 2: Ordering and rounding

1. Estimate the answer to each calculation.

   a 6.75 × 2.98

   b 9.72 ÷ 2.16

   c 0.85 + 12.07

   d 1.98 × 2.3 × 4.65

2. It costs £2.95 for a bus ticket. Estimate how many bus tickets you can buy for £12.

3. A DVD costs £5.99. Estimate how many DVDs you can buy for £25.

4. A theatre ticket costs £11.90. Estimate how many tickets you can buy for £50.

5. Estimate the cost of 2.8 kg of apples at £1.88 per kilogram.

6. Estimate the cost of 7.15 m of fabric at £9.25 per metre.

7. Estimate the cost of 11.25 litres of olive oil at £4.92 per litre.

TASK 3: Mental calculations

Example

Work out: **a** 2.4 + 3.7   **b** 8.4 − 5.6

A number line helps you to work out sums and differences.
Deal with the whole-number part first.

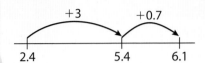

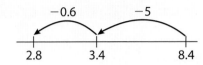

① In a magic square, each row, column and diagonal adds up to the same total.
Copy and complete these magic squares.

a

6	...	...
...	4	...
3	...	2

b

0.5	...	0.2
...	0.4	...
0.6	...	...

c

...	0.3	...
...	3.0	...
...	5.7	1.5

d

2.7	...	...
...	2.1	...
2.1	...	1.5

TASK 4: Written calculations

 Points to remember

For column addition and subtraction of decimals:

⊙ line up the decimal points, write tenths under tenths, hundredths under hundredths, and so on;

⊙ fill the gaps at the end of the decimal places with zeros if you wish;

⊙ show 'carry' figures clearly;

⊙ change units of measurement to the same unit.

For multiplication of whole numbers in columns:

⊙ estimate the answer first;

⊙ line up units under units, tens under tens, and so on;

⊙ compare the answer with the estimate.

1. In the diagram, any three numbers in a line, across or down, have the same total. Work out the missing number.

4.92	11.07	2.46
3.69		8.61
9.84	1.23	7.38

2. Find the total cost of these items.

> 4 shelves at £2.35 each
>
> 8 brackets at 41p each
>
> 5 packets of screws at £1.06 each
>
> 1 tube of glue at 58p

3. Work out each of these multiplication problems.

   a 59×73 b 67×984

4. Kate knows that

$$137 \times 28 = 3836$$

Explain how she can use this information to work out this multiplication.

$$138 \times 28$$

TASK 5: Using a calculator

 Points to remember

When you use a calculator:

- estimate the result of a calculation and check the answer against the estimate;
- check a one-step calculation by working the problem backwards;
- use the CLEAR-ALL key before each new calculation;
- use the CLEAR key to clear the last entry.

(1) **Use your calculator** to work out each of these.

a $\sqrt{72.25}$

b $\sqrt{28.09}$

c 3.6^2

d 5.8^2

e $\sqrt{(33.8 + 56.45)}$

f $\sqrt{(8 - 6.04)}$

g $(6.2 - 2.8)^2$

h $(3.5 + 5.1)^2$

i $8.7 - (6.2 - 1.9)$

j $6.3 \times (7.5 + 5.6)$

k $\dfrac{9.7 - 4.8}{0.7}$

l $\dfrac{23.25}{6 \times 0.25}$

(2) The corner shop sells sheets of stamps.
On each sheet there are 36 rows and 18 columns of stamps.
How many stamps are there altogether on 45 sheets?

(3) When you change euros to pounds you get 67p for each euro.
How much do you get when you change 45 euros to pounds?

TASK 6: Problem solving

 Points to remember

When you solve problems using your calculator:

⊙ work systematically;

⊙ keep a careful record of your findings as you go along;

⊙ look for patterns in your findings and draw on these to come to some conclusions that you can explain and justify.

Use your calculator to help you to answer these questions.

(1) 2, 3 and 5 are three prime numbers.
Their product is 30.

$$2 \times 3 \times 5 = 30$$

Find three prime numbers with a product of 231.

(2) In these calculations, each ★ stands for a missing digit.
Find the missing digits.

a ★3 × 59 = 767

b ★★ × ★ = 378

(3) In these calculations, the signs $+$, $-$, $\times$ or $\div$ have been replaced with a ●.
Rewrite the calculations, replacing each ● with the correct sign.

a 47 ● 23 ● 27 ● 15 = 112

b 34 ● (37 ● 18) = 700

c 768 ● (43 ● 37) = 128

d 1116 ● (23 ● 47) = 35

Area and perimeter

TASK 1: Area and perimeter of rectangles

> ### ◉ Points to remember
>
> - ⊙ **Perimeter** is the distance around the outside of a shape.
> - ⊙ **Area** is a measure of the surface covered by a shape.
> - ⊙ Area is always measured in square units.
> - ⊙ Area of a rectangle = length × width.
> - ⊙ Change units of length to the same unit before you do any calculations.

1. A rectangular field in this photograph is 200 m long and 90 m wide.

   a What is the perimeter of the field?

   b What is the area of the field?

   c Another rectangular field has an area of 15 000 m². The field is 150 m long. How wide is it?

2. Work out the perimeter and area of each of the rectangles A, B and C.

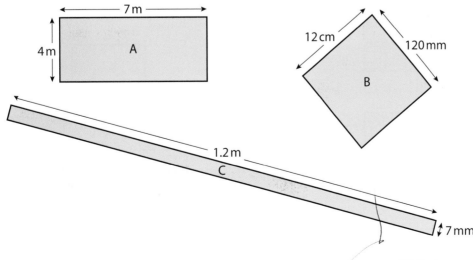

(3) The perimeter of this rectangle is 24 cm.
What is the area of the rectangle?

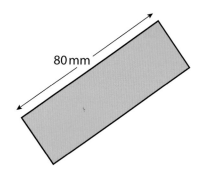

80 mm

TASK 2: Irregular shapes

You may **use your calculator**.

(1) Find the area of the shaded part of each diagram.

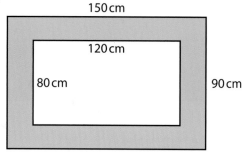

a

150 cm

120 cm

80 cm

90 cm

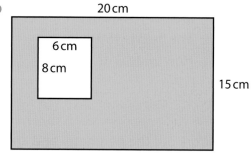

b

20 cm

6 cm

8 cm

15 cm

(2) Calculate the perimeter and area of each of these shapes.

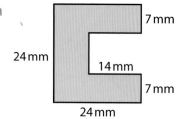

a

7 mm

24 mm

14 mm

7 mm

24 mm

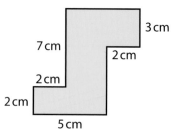

b

3 cm

7 cm

2 cm

2 cm

2 cm

5 cm

TASK 3: Surface area of cuboids

You will need squared paper for question 1.

1. Draw a net of this cuboid.
   Mark the measurements on your net.

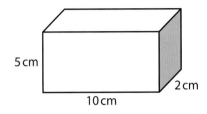

5 cm   2 cm   10 cm

2. Work out the surface area of the cuboid in question 1.

3. This cube is made from 2 cm by 2 cm by 2 cm small cubes.
   a What is the surface area of the large cube?
   b What is the surface area of a small cube?

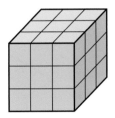

4. This shape is made from two cuboids.
   Calculate its surface area.

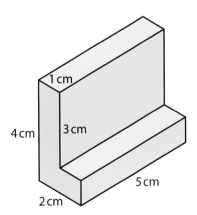

1 cm   4 cm   3 cm   5 cm   2 cm

TASK 4: 3D shapes

You will need some triangular dotty paper.

1. How many cubes would you need to make each of these shapes?

a 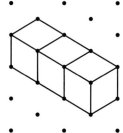 b 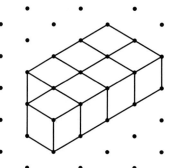 c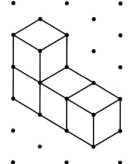

d 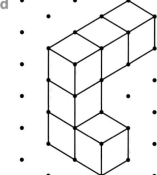 e 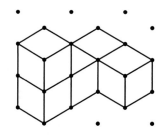 f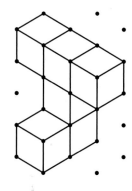

2. Each of the cubes in question 1 is 1 cm by 1 cm by 1 cm.
   What is the surface area of each shape?

Fractions and percentages

TASK 1: Fractions of shapes

> **Points to remember**
>
> ⊙ If $\frac{3}{8}$ of a shape is shaded, then $\frac{5}{8}$ is not shaded.
>
> If $\frac{2}{5}$ of a class are girls, then $\frac{3}{5}$ are boys.
>
> ⊙ Some fractions can be written more simply.
>
> $\frac{5}{10}$, $\frac{4}{8}$, $\frac{3}{6}$ and $\frac{2}{4}$ are all the same as $\frac{1}{2}$.
>
> $\frac{3}{12}$ and $\frac{2}{8}$ are both the same as $\frac{1}{4}$.

1 Look at these shapes.

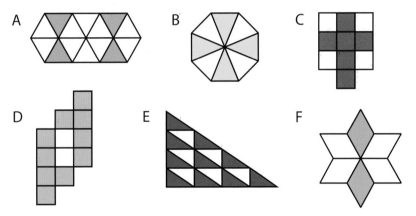

Write the letter of the shape that has:

a one half shaded   b one third shaded   c three fifths shaded

d five eighths shaded   e five sixths shaded   f two sevenths shaded

2 Imagine you have these five cards.

Make fractions using one card for the numerator and one for the denominator.
How many different fractions less than one half can you make with the cards?
Write each fraction as simply as you can.

TASK 2: Equivalent fractions

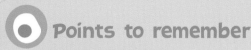

Points to remember

⊙ To **simplify** or **cancel** a fraction, divide the numerator and denominator by the same number.

Example: $\dfrac{^210}{^315} = \dfrac{2}{3}$

⊙ To find an equivalent fraction, multiply or divide the numerator and denominator by the same number.

Example: $\dfrac{3}{4} = \dfrac{3 \times 5}{4 \times 5} = \dfrac{15}{20}$

⊙ An **improper fraction** has a numerator that is bigger than the denominator.

⊙ A **mixed number** has a whole-number part and a fraction part.

① Write these as mixed numbers.

   a $\dfrac{11}{4}$ **b** $\dfrac{8}{3}$ **c** $\dfrac{12}{5}$ **d** $\dfrac{21}{7}$

② Write these as improper fractions.

   a $5\frac{2}{3}$ **b** $3\frac{4}{5}$ **c** $6\frac{3}{10}$ **d** $4\frac{5}{7}$

③ Use each of the digits 2, 3 and 5 for each fraction that you make.

$$\boxed{2}\quad\boxed{3}\quad\boxed{5}$$

Make improper fractions that have a two-digit numerator and a one-digit denominator.

How many different improper fractions can you make?
Write each of these improper fractions as a mixed number.

TASK 3: Changing fractions to decimals

Points to remember

- To change a fraction to a decimal, divide the numerator by the denominator. You can use a calculator to do this.

  Examples: $\frac{3}{20} = 3 \div 20 = 0.15$ $\frac{5}{80} = 5 \div 80 = 0.0625$

- To change a decimal to a fraction, consider the tenths, hundredths and thousandths.

  Example: $0.627 = 0.6 + 0.02 + 0.007$

  $0.627 = \frac{6}{10} + \frac{2}{100} + \frac{7}{1000} = \frac{627}{1000}$

- Equivalent fractions are represented by the same decimal number.

You may **use your calculator**.

1. Pick out the biggest fraction from each pair.

   a $\frac{1}{2}$ and $\frac{1}{3}$ b $\frac{1}{4}$ and $\frac{1}{3}$ c $\frac{2}{3}$ and $\frac{3}{4}$ d $\frac{2}{3}$ and $\frac{5}{8}$

2. Danny has a set of measuring jugs that he uses when he is cooking.

0.75 litre	0.6 litre	0.45 litre	0.425 litre
0.375 litre	0.35 litre	0.3 litre	0.275 litre

   Which jug should Danny use to measure these amounts of milk?

   a $\frac{3}{10}$ of a litre   b $\frac{3}{5}$ of a litre   c $\frac{9}{20}$ of a litre   d $\frac{3}{8}$ of a litre

3. Amrita has 12 cards.
   She matches the fractions to the decimals to make six pairs.
   Which cards did Amrita pair up?

$\frac{10}{11}$	$\frac{2}{9}$	$\frac{5}{8}$	$\frac{5}{6}$	$\frac{1}{7}$	$\frac{4}{7}$

   0.5714285   0.1428571   0.2222222

   0.8333333   0.625

   0.9090909

TASK 4: Equivalent fractions, decimals and percentages

Points to remember

⊙ **Percentage** means 'per hundred', or 'in every hundred'.
This table shows some percentage, fraction and decimal equivalents.

1%	$\frac{1}{100}$	0.01
10%	$\frac{1}{10}$	0.1
47%	$\frac{47}{100}$	0.47
50%	$\frac{50}{100} = \frac{1}{2}$	0.5
25%	$\frac{25}{100} = \frac{1}{4}$	0.25
75%	$\frac{75}{100} = \frac{3}{4}$	0.75

⊙ It is easy to write a percentage as a fraction or decimal.
Example: 47% can be written as $\frac{47}{100}$ or as 0.47.

⊙ To change a decimal to a percentage, multiply it by 100.
Examples: 0.76 is 76%, because $0.76 \times 100 = 76$.
1.234 is 123.4%, because $1.234 \times 100 = 123.4$.

⊙ To change a fraction to a percentage, change it to a decimal, then multiply it by 100.
Example: $\frac{3}{10}$ as a percentage is $0.3 \times 100\% = 30\%$.

① What percentage of this shape is shaded?

② One quarter of the pupils in a class wear glasses.
What percentage do not wear glasses?

③ 80% of the pupils in class walk to school.
What fraction do not walk to school?

④ Pick out the bigger number from each pair.

    a $\frac{1}{4}$ and 0.4   b $\frac{1}{5}$ and 0.5   c $\frac{1}{3}$ and 0.3

    d $\frac{2}{5}$ and 0.5   e $\frac{1}{5}$ and 0.15   f $\frac{1}{8}$ and 0.18

TASK 5: Adding and subtracting simple fractions

 Points to remember

⊙ When you add or subtract fractions, they must have the same denominator.

To make the denominators the same before adding or subtracting fractions, find the lowest common multiple of the two denominators.

Example 1   Work out $\frac{1}{3} + \frac{1}{4}$.

The lowest common multiple of 3 and 4 is 12, so change both fractions to twelfths.

$$\frac{1}{3} + \frac{1}{4} = \frac{4}{12} + \frac{3}{12} = \frac{7}{12}$$

The numerator of the answer is the sum of the numerators of the two fractions.

The denominator does not change.

Sometimes you can cancel the answer to its simplest form.

Example 2 $\frac{5}{12} - \frac{1}{6} = \frac{5}{12} - \frac{2}{12} = \frac{^1\cancel{3}}{^4\cancel{12}} = \frac{1}{4}$

The answer to each calculation is $\frac{1}{2}$.
Find the fraction represented by each letter.
Show all your working.

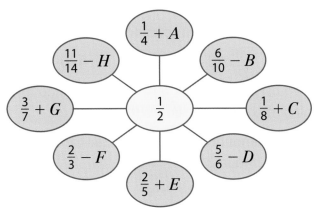

TASK 6: Fractions of whole-number quantities

 Points to remember

- To find $\frac{1}{8}$, divide by 8.
- To find $\frac{3}{8}$, find $\frac{1}{8}$ and multiply it by 3.
- To find $\frac{1}{4}$, find one half of one half.
- To find $\frac{3}{4}$, work out $\frac{1}{4}$ then multiply it by 3.

Example   What is $\frac{3}{5}$ of £30?

To find $\frac{3}{5}$, find one fifth by dividing by 5, then find three fifths by multiplying by 3.

(Find $\frac{1}{5}$) $30 \div 5 = 6$

(Find $\frac{3}{15}$) $6 \times 3 = 18$ Answer: £18

1. I filled each of 5 cups with two fifths of a litre of lemonade.
   How much lemonade did I use?

2. Molly spent three fifths of her savings of £100.
   How much money did she have left?

3. How much more is two fifths of a litre than three eighths of a litre?
   Give your answer in millilitres.

4. Gail is taking part in a game show.
   She has been shown three amounts of money.

   £240   £360   £480

   For her prize, she must choose three quarters of one amount, two thirds of another amount, and half of the remaining amount.

   What is the maximum amount of money that Gail can win as a prize?
   What is the minimum amount?
   Explain your reasoning.

TASK 7: Percentages of whole-number quantities

Example   Find 24% of £60.

1% of £60 is £60 ÷ 100 = £0.60

24% of £60 is £0.60 × 24 = £14.40

1   A shop is taking 10% off all its prices.
    What will these cost after the 10% discount?

   a   Shirt £20   b   Tie £5

   c   Trousers £32   d   Socks 90p

   e   Shoes £25.50   f   Jacket £42.30

2   A company is giving its workers a 5% pay increase.
    How much will these people earn after the pay rise?

   a   Office manager £25 000   b   Secretary £12 500

   c   Regional manager £50 000   d   Sales representative £18 000

   e   Filing clerk £8000   f   Telephone receptionist £10 500

3   Which of these cars is cheaper after the discount?

B

A

10% off usual price of £15 500

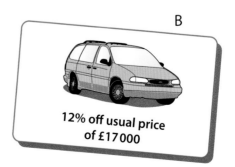

12% off usual price of £17 000

Grouped data and simple statistics

TASK 1: Constructing charts and tables

⊙ Points to remember

- ⊙ Leave equal spaces between the bars or lines on a graph.
- ⊙ Label lines, not spaces, on the frequency axis.
- ⊙ Groups of data should not overlap.
- ⊙ The **modal class** is the group that occurs most often.

Examples

This is a **bar-line graph**.
It shows the scores when a dice is rolled 50 times.

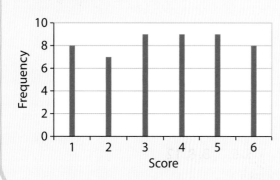

This is a **frequency diagram**.
It shows the number of journeys some people make by car in a week.

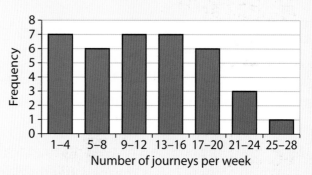

You will need squared paper.

1. A computer is used to generate random numbers between 1 and 10 for a game.
   This table shows the first 40 numbers generated by the computer.

Score	1	2	3	4	5	6	7	8	9	10
Frequency	3	6	4	5	3	4	2	6	3	4

   Draw a bar-line graph for the data.
   Use a vertical frequency scale numbered in 1s.
   Space the bar-lines at 1 cm intervals horizontally.

(2) The table shows how many times some people exercised in a week.

Number of times	1–3	4–6	7–9	10–12	13–15	16–18	19–21
Frequency	8	12	6	5	5	2	1

Draw a frequency diagram for the data.
Use a vertical frequency scale numbered in 1s.
Space the bars at 1 cm intervals horizontally. Make the bars 1 cm wide.

TASK 2: Calculating statistics

⦿ Points to remember

⦿ An **average** is a number that represents all the numbers in a set.
  - The **mode** is the number that occurs most often in the set.
  - To find the **mean**, add up all the numbers in the set and divide by the number of numbers in the set.
  - The **median** is the middle number, or the mean of the middle two numbers, when you put all the numbers in the set in order.
⦿ The **range** is the largest number in a set minus the smallest number.

Example

In the set of numbers 3, 8, 5, 6, 8, 12, 7:

Mode = 8   The number that occurs most often is 8.

Mean = 7 $3 + 8 + 5 + 6 + 8 + 12 + 7 = 49$
              $49 \div 7 = 7$

Median = 7   The numbers in ascending order are 3, 5, 6, **7**, 8, 8, 12

Range = 5   The highest value − the lowest value = $12 - 3 = 9$

(1) Write down the first names of ten of your friends.
Count the number of letters in each name. Write this number next to the name.

   a What is the mean number of letters in your friends' names?
   b What is the median?
   c What is the mode?
   d What is the range?

(2) Repeat question 1 but this time use the last names of ten of your friends.

(3) Which is longer on average, a person's first name or their last name?

TASK 3: Interpreting graphs and diagrams

 Points to remember

- Different types of graph are used for different types of data and show different information.
- A **bar chart** or **bar-line graph** shows:
  - the frequency of items in each category or group of data;
  - the total frequency of all the items of data.

  A **pie chart** does not show this information.
- Use a **pie chart** to show and compare the proportion of each category of data.

Example

The frequency diagram shows the number of journeys some people made by car in a week. The graph shows that most people made 20 or fewer journeys – less than three a day. Only one person made more than 24 journeys.

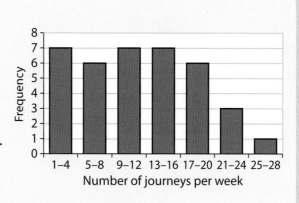

The number of journeys people made varied widely.

1. A computer generates random numbers between 1 and 10 for a game. The bar-line graph shows the first 40 numbers generated by the computer.

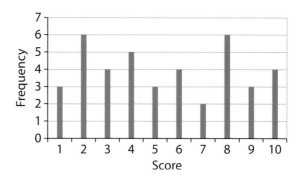

   a Which numbers occurred most often?

   b Which number occurred least often?

   c Write a sentence to say what the graph shows.

   d Fernando needs 11 on his next turn in order to win the game. Can he win on his next turn?

2 The frequency diagram shows the results of a survey.
It shows how many times people exercised in a week.

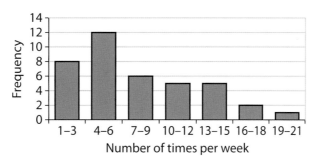

a Which is the modal group?
Roughly how many times a day did this group of people exercise?

b How many people altogether took part in the survey?

3 The pie chart shows the results of a survey in 2005.
It shows the percentage of people viewing each TV channel.

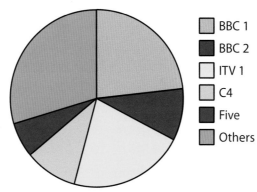

Source: www.barb.co.uk

a Write a sentence to say what the pie chart shows.

b Which two of the named channels had the largest share of the viewing?
Roughly what percentage did they have in total?

G 3.2 Angles

TASK 1: Measuring and drawing angles

> ### ● Points to remember
>
> ⊙ An angle is a measure of **turn**.
> ⊙ There are 360° in one whole turn.
> ⊙ An **acute angle** is between 0° and 90°.
> ⊙ An **obtuse angle** is between 90° and 180°.
> ⊙ An angle between 180° and 360° is a **reflex angle**.
> ⊙ When you measure an angle:
>   – first estimate its size;
>   – line up the protractor correctly;
>   – use the correct scale on the protractor.

(1) **a** Measure each of the angles a, b and c.

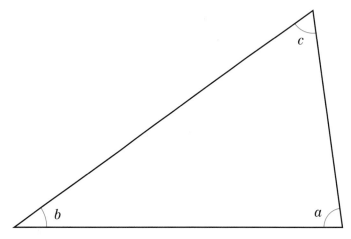

b Work out the sum of the angles a, b and c.

(2) Use a protractor, ruler and sharp pencil.
Draw each of these angles.

    a 50°   **b** 130°   **c** 200°

TASK 2: Angles on a straight line

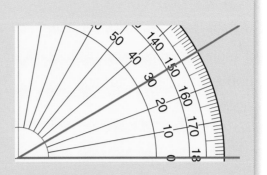
1) Calculate the size of each angle marked with a letter.
   Give your reasons.

a

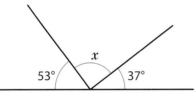

53°   x   37°

b

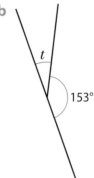

t

153°

c

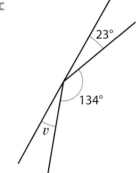

23°

134°

v

2) In the diagram, angle ADC = 35° and angle CDE = 85°.
   Find angle EDB.
   Give reasons for your answer.

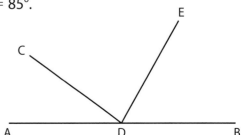

TASK 3: Angles at a point

Points to remember

- The sum of angles on a straight line is 180°.
- The sum of angles at a point is 360°.
- Vertically opposite angles are equal.
- When you calculate angles, give your reasons.

(1) Find the size of each angle marked with a letter.
Give your reasons for your answers.

a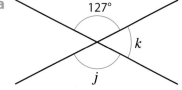

b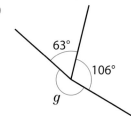

c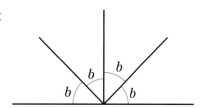

(2) In this diagram MN and PQ are straight lines.
Angle PSM is 50°.
Angle RSN is 90°.
Angle QST is 70°.

a Find the size of angle QSN.

b Find the size of angle RSP.

c Find the size of angle MST.

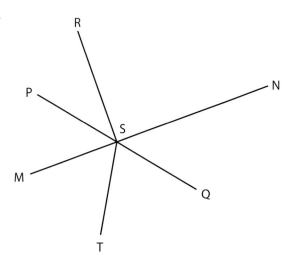

Probability 1

TASK 1: The probability scale

> ### Points to remember
>
> ⊙ Probability can be described using words such as:
>
>   **impossible   unlikely   even chance   likely   certain**
>
>   The word 'chance' is also used to describe probability.
>
> ⊙ Probability is measured on a scale from 0 (impossible) to 1 (certain).
>
> | impossible | unlikely | even chance | likely | certain |
> |---|---|---|---|---|
> | 0 | | $\frac{1}{2}$ | | 1 |

① Use one of the probability terms below to describe the likelihood of each event **a** to **d**.

impossible   very unlikely   unlikely   even chance   likely   very likely   certain

   a It is my headteacher's birthday
      tomorrow.

   b My school will be open tomorrow.

   c I will have my favourite meal to
      eat tonight.

   d I will see Queen Victoria on my way
      home from school.

② Write down an event that is:

   a certain   **b** very likely   **c** very unlikely   **d** impossible

TASK 2: Equally likely outcomes

⊙ Points to remember

⊙ You can use fractions to describe probabilities.
For example, a chance of 1 in 3 is a probability of $\frac{1}{3}$.

⊙ **Equally likely outcomes** have the same chance of happening.

For example, a coin has two equally likely outcomes, **heads** and **tails**.
The probability of getting a head is $\frac{1}{2}$ and of getting a tail is $\frac{1}{2}$.

1. You will need a coin, a counter (or something similar) and **S3.2 Resource sheet 2.2**.

   ▶ Place your counter on the START square on the grid on the resource sheet.

   ▶ Flip the coin.
   If you get **heads**, move one square right.
   If you get **tails**, move one square up.

   ▶ Mark the squares on the grid as you move.

   Where would you expect to finish? Explain why.

Example

Helen flipped a coin.
She got head, head, tail, head, tail, head.
Here is part of her grid.

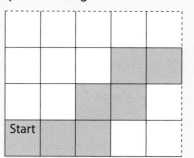

TASK 3: Probability experiments

⊙ Points to remember

⊙ You can estimate probability from an experiment.

⊙ The estimate may not be the same as the probability you calculate equally likely outcomes.

Example

You toss a coin 10 times. You get a head 3 times.

The experimental probability of getting a head is $\frac{3}{10}$.

You will need a penny and a copy of **S3.2 Resource sheet 3.2**. Follow the instructions on the resource sheet.

Decimals and measures

TASK 1: Estimating and converting measurements

⊙ Points to remember

⊙ Use this diagram to help you to convert units of **length**.

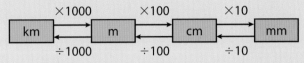

⊙ These diagrams will help you to convert units of **mass** or **capacity**.

⊙ This diagram will help you to convert units of **area**.

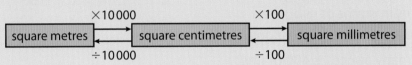

1. a Write 78 mm in centimetres.
    b Write 3.5 km in metres.
    c Write 483 mm in metres.
    d Write 2.8 m in centimetres.
    e Write 0.5 km in centimetres.
    f Write 8345 m in kilometres.
    g Write 730 cm in metres.
    h Write 4.76 m in millimetres.

2. a Write 326 ml in litres.
    b Write 0.8 kg in grams.
    c Write 50 g in kilograms.
    d Write 4.1 litres in millilitres.
    e Write 0.25 kg in grams.
    f Write 600 ml in litres.

3. a Write 5 m^2 in square centimetres.
    b Write 375 mm^2 in square centimetres.
    c Write 6000 cm^2 in square metres.
    d Write 0.75 cm^2 in square millimetres.

TASK 2: Reading scales

 Points to remember

To work out the quantity represented by an interval on a scale:

⊙ find two numbered divisions;

⊙ work out their difference;

⊙ divide the difference by the number of intervals between the divisions.

1 The diagram shows the volume of water
   in two measuring jugs.

   a Which jug contains less water, A or B?

   b How much less does it contain?

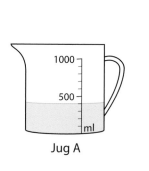

Jug A

Jug B

2 A scale measures in grams or in ounces.
   Use the scale to answer these questions.

   a About how many ounces is 400 grams?

   b About how many grams is 8 ounces?

   c About how many ounces is 1 kilogram?
      Explain your answer.

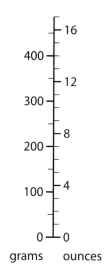

3 The diagram shows part of
   a ruler.

   a What is the distance
      between A and B?

   b What is the distance
      between C and D?

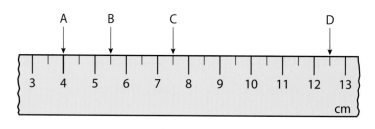

TASK 3: Solving word problems

● Points to remember

To solve word problems:

- ⊙ look out for key words that help to decide what operation(s) to do;
- ⊙ change all measurements to the same unit;
- ⊙ check your answer and make sure it is sensible in the context;
- ⊙ include any units in the answer.

Do question 1 **without using a calculator**. Show your working.

1 a   Mark's height is 0.8 m. Anna is 40 cm taller than Mark. What is Anna's height?

  b   Tim's height is 1.45 m. Sally is 30 cm shorter than Tim. What is Sally's height?

  c   Pam's height is 1.7 m. What is Pam's height in centimetres?

For the rest of the questions, you may **use a calculator**.

2   A family pack contains bags of crisps.
    Each bag of crisps weighs 25 grams.
    Altogether, the bags of crisps in the pack weigh 0.5 kg.
    How many bags of crisps are in the pack?

3   Jack needs half a litre of lemon juice to make a fruit drink
    for a party.
    He squeezes 14 lemons.
    Each lemon gives him 35 ml of juice.
    Does Jack have enough lemon juice for his fruit drink?

4   Rupee has a piece of cheese that weighs 0.6 kg.
    She cuts off 3 slices, each weighing 90 g.
    How much cheese is left?

5   Each paper clip is made from 9.2 centimetres of wire.
    What is the greatest number of paper clips that can be made
    from 10 metres of wire?

TASK 4: Problems involving time

Points to remember

⊙ 13:26 means 1:26 pm, and 06:45 means 6:45 am.

⊙ Time lines are useful for working out time intervals.

(1) A cookery book gives these times for cooking meat:

> Lamb: 20 minutes plus 15 minutes for each 250 g.
> Chicken: 30 minutes plus 10 minutes for each 250 g.

Copy and complete this table of cooking times.

Weight of meat	0.5 kg	0.75 kg	1 kg	1.25 kg	1.5 kg	1.75 kg
Cooking time: lamb	50 minutes					
Cooking time: chicken	50 minutes					

Use the completed table to work out answers to these questions.

(2) I put a 1.5 kg joint of lamb in the oven at 13:30.
At what time will it be ready?

(3) I want to cook 750 g of chicken to be ready for a meal at 18:15. At what time must I start to cook it?

(4) A 1 kg joint of lamb was cooked by 19:20.
At what time did it go in the oven?

(5) A 1.25 kg chicken went in the oven at 11:45 am.
When will it be cooked?

TASK 5: Multiplication and division calculations

Points to remember

⊙ First see if you can do a calculation in your head.

⊙ Use an efficient written method if no calculator is available.

⊙ Always estimate the answer to multiplication and division calculations.

⊙ Check the answer by using the inverse operation.

1. Find pairs of consecutive numbers to complete these products. You may **use a calculator**.

   a □ × □ = 90
   b □ × □ = 210
   c □ × □ = 342
   d □ × □ = 756
   e □ × □ = 1892
   f □ × □ = 3306

2. **Without using a calculator**, do these calculations. Show your working.

   a 192 × 18
   b 992 ÷ 31
   c 910 ÷ 35
   d 884 ÷ 52
   e 46.3 × 12
   f 9.87 ÷ 47

TASK 6: Solving problems with a calculator

● Points to remember

To use the memory of your calculator, follow these steps.

Step 1: Clear the memory.

Step 2: Enter the number (or enter a calculation and press ⌷=⌷).

Step 3: Press ⌷M+⌷ to add the number (or the answer) to the memory.

Step 4: Clear the display by pressing the clear key (there will be a small M to show that there is a number in the memory).

Step 5: Repeat steps 2 to 4 as often as needed.

Step 6: Press the memory recall button. The total will appear.

1. Sandra throws six darts at this dartboard.
   Each dart lands on the board.
   More than one dart can land on a number.

   Sandra scores exactly 200.
   How did she do it?

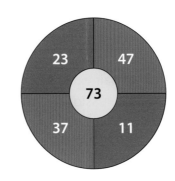

2. What missing number goes in each box?

   a 8.5 × □ = 404.09
   b 10 233 ÷ □ = 379
   c □ × 32.45 = 253.11
   d □ ÷ 18.5 = 36.4
   e 568.1 = 24.7 × □
   f 49.5 = 950.4 ÷ □

Equations and formulae

TASK 1: Terms and expressions

◉ Points to remember

- ⊙ $3n + 5$ is an **expression**. An algebraic expression must contain at least one letter.
- ⊙ Each part of an expression is called a **term** of the expression. For example, for the expression $3n + 5$ the terms are $3n$ and 5.
- ⊙ **Like terms** have the same combination of letters. For example, $2x$ and $5x$ and x are all like terms.

① There are p big boats and q small boats in a harbour.

   a Write an expression for the total number of boats in the harbour.

   b 15 boats leave the harbour.

     Write an expression for the total number of boats in the harbour now.

② Greg used n tins of paint to paint his small boat.
Each tin of paint cost £12.
Write an expression for the total cost of the tins of paint that Greg used.

③ Copy these expressions and underline each term.

   a $8 + 3x$ **b** $4y + 7z - 4w$

   c $3ab + 4bc + 9ac + 5$ **d** $9ax + 14by + 17ab$

④ Simplify each expression by collecting like terms.

   a $2a + 5a + 7a$ **b** $13b + 9b - 14b$

   c $7x - x + 5x + 8$ **d** $19 + 3x + 15 - 2x$

TASK 2: Multiplying terms in brackets

Point to remember

⊙ $7(n + 6)$ means 7 times n and 7 times 6.

×	n	+	6
7	$7n$	+	42

1. Multiply out these brackets.

   a $8(n + 5)$ b $7(n + 10)$ c $9(x + 9)$

   d $2(9y + 10)$ e $5(4x + 6y)$ f $3(5w + 6x + 7y)$

2. Simplify each expression by collecting like terms.

   a $h + 5h + 7$ b $3b + 6b - 4b$

   c $7x + 1 - 7x + 2$ d $4m + 3n + 2m - 2n$

TASK 3: Formulae

Points to remember

⊙ A **formula** is a way of writing a rule using letters.
For example, the formula for working out the area A of a rectangle with length l and width w is

$$A = lw$$

1. Let n be the number of miles that Tim travels to school each day.

   Tim asked five friends how far they travelled to school.

   Write a formula using n for the distances that each of Tim's friends travels.

   a Sean travels twice as far as Tim.

   b Kate travels three miles more than Tim.

   c Paul travels two miles less than Tim.

   d Nan travels half as far as Tim.

   e Andrew travels two miles less than Kate.

2 A formula for the area A of a triangle is

$$A = \tfrac{1}{2}bh$$

where b is the length of the base and h is the height.

Work out the area of these triangles (lengths are in cm).

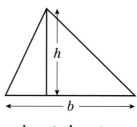

    a $b = 12$, $h = 7$ **b** $b = 20$, $h = 8$ **c** $b = 6$, $h = 6$

TASK 4: Equations: addition and subtraction

⊙ Points to remember

- This is an equation: $x + 8 = 12$. It has one solution, $x = 4$.
- This is an equation: $x - 5 = 3$. It has one solution, $x = 8$.

1 Find the value of x for each of these.

    a $x + 5 = 8$ **b** $x + 7 = 15$ **c** $x + 9 = 21$

    d $x + 16 = 32$ **e** $x + 43 = 57$ **f** $x + 1.2 = 2.5$

2 Find the value of x for each of these.

    a $x - 7 = 10$ **b** $x - 3 = 5$ **c** $x - 6 = 12$

    d $x - 8 = 15$ **e** $x - 10 = 10$ **f** $x - 2.5 = 3.5$

TASK 5: Equations: multiplication and division

⊙ Points to remember

- This is an equation: $4x = 12$. It has one solution, $x = 3$.
- This is an equation: $x \div 5 = 2$. It has one solution, $x = 10$.

1 Find the value of x.

    a $6x = 42$ **b** $10x = 90$ **c** $9x = 72$

    d $5x = 15$ **e** $7x = 49$ **f** $8x = 32$

2 Find the value of x.

    a $x \div 7 = 3$ **b** $x \div 10 = 4$ **c** $x \div 6 = 8$

    d $x \div 9 = 7$ **e** $x \div 11 = 5$ **f** $x \div 2 = 22$

Enquiry 1

TASK 1: Planning a project

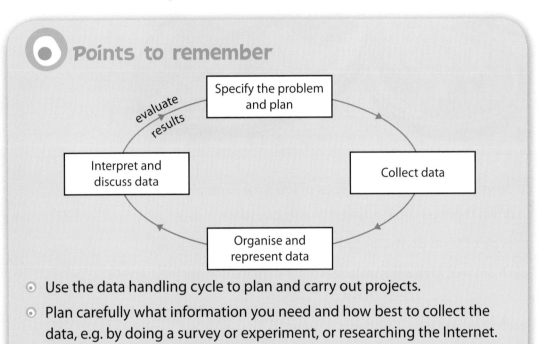

Points to remember

- Specify the problem and plan
- evaluate results
- Collect data
- Interpret and discuss data
- Organise and represent data

- ⊙ Use the data handling cycle to plan and carry out projects.
- ⊙ Plan carefully what information you need and how best to collect the data, e.g. by doing a survey or experiment, or researching the Internet.
- ⊙ Then collect and organise the data.

1 Imagine that pupils in your class have been considering this question:

   'What type of holiday would you most like to go on?'

   a Write down five different types of holiday, for example, beach holiday or camping.

   b Write down three possible answers to the question in purple above.

   Give a possible reason or explanation for each of your answers.

(2)

a   Write down five or six different types of food, for example, chilli or pizza.

b   Write down three possible answers to this question:

What type of food do the people in your class like the most?

For each answer, give a possible reason or explanation for your answer.

(3)   Match each question with a possible answer.

Example: A possible answer to 'What is the favourite colour of pupils in my class?' is 'blue'.
An impossible answer to the same question is 'pizza'.

Questions

a   What is the most common form of transport used by pupils in my class to get to school?

b   What is the favourite food of pupils in my class?

c   Do boys or girls take the most exercise?

d   What do children spend their pocket money on?

e   What is the favourite vegetable of pupils in your class?

f   Which country has the greatest rate of population growth?

Possible answers
Comics
Boys
Carrots
Walk
Afghanistan
Pizza

TASK 2: Collecting data 1

 Points to remember

- ⊙ Plan carefully how you will collect the data.
- ⊙ When you write a questionnaire, think about the choices you offer.
- ⊙ Where numerical data varies widely, group the data for analysis.

Collect some data to add to that collected in class.

① Collect and record the shoe sizes of between five and eight people.

② Show this diagram for a few seconds to between five and eight people.

Ask them to estimate the number of dots.

Record the estimates.

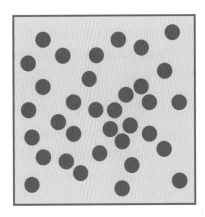

TASK 3: Drawing charts and graphs

 Points to remember

- ⊙ Graphs and charts help to show features of a set of data.
- ⊙ A bar-line graph is like a bar chart with very thin bars.
- ⊙ A frequency diagram is a type of bar chart used for grouped data.

Example

Draw a bar-line graph to show pupils' favourite ways to travel.

Travel type	Frequency
Car	12
Aeroplane	8
Helicopter	2
Boat	4
Limousine	2
Time machine	1

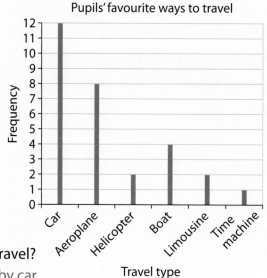

Pupils' favourite ways to travel

a What was the favourite way to travel?

The favourite way to travel was by car.

b How many pupils were asked? 29

c Fill in the gaps in this sentence.

… times as many pupils prefer to travel by car than by helicopter.

Six times as many pupils prefer to travel by car than by helicopter.

---

1 The results of a survey showing the colours of cars in a car park are given in the frequency table.

a Draw a bar-line graph to show this data.

b What is the most popular colour of car?

c Write the colours of the cars in order of popularity, the most popular first.

Colour	Frequency
Black	8
Blue	12
Green	7
Gold	1
Grey	2
Red	15
Silver	29
White	26

2 The pie chart shows the results of a survey of the type of breakfast children had.

a What was the most usual breakfast?

b Roughly what percentage of children had no breakfast?

c Did more children have toast or a cooked breakfast?

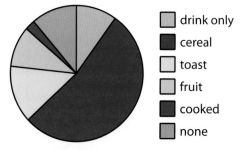

Types of breakfast for a group of pupils

- drink only
- cereal
- toast
- fruit
- cooked
- none

Adapted from www.food.gov.uk

TASK 4: Collecting data 2

Points to remember

- A questionnaire should have clear instructions so that people know how to answer the questions.

Fill in your copy of the class questionnaire about planning a year-group visit.

TASK 5: Interpreting charts and graphs

Points to remember

- Graphs and charts help to show features of a set of data.
- The shape of the graph can also help you to interpret the data.
- Acknowledge the source of data that you collect from the Internet or books.

1 The frequency table shows the number of letters in the words from a page in a book.

Number of letters	Frequency
1–3	17
4–6	15
7–9	6
10–12	1

  a Draw a frequency diagram to illustrate this data.

  b How many words were there altogether?

  c How many letters do you think there are in the longest word?

2 The pie chart shows the results of a survey on sandwich fillings.

  a Write down two sandwich fillings that between them make up more than half of the sandwiches.

  b Which is the least popular sandwich filling listed?

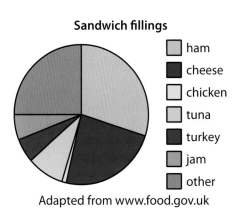

Sandwich fillings

- ham
- cheese
- chicken
- tuna
- turkey
- jam
- other

Adapted from www.food.gov.uk

Functions and graphs

TASK 1: Functions and mappings

 Points to remember

- A function machine applies a rule or **function** to an **input** x and gives the related **output** y.
- This **mapping diagram** shows the relationship between x and y:

  $x \rightarrow y$

  $2 \rightarrow 5$

  $3 \rightarrow 7$

  $4 \rightarrow 9$

  $x \rightarrow 2x + 1$
- If the function is 'add 3', the inverse function is 'subtract 3'.
- If the function is 'multiply by 5', the inverse function is 'divide by 5'.

1 Find the outputs y for the given inputs x for this function machine.

$x \rightarrow \boxed{\text{subtract 4}} \rightarrow y$

a $x = 11$ b $x = 30$ c $x = 8$ d $x = 16$

2 Find the outputs y for the given inputs x for this function machine.

$x \rightarrow \boxed{\text{multiply by 3}} \rightarrow \boxed{\text{add 2}} \rightarrow y$

a $x = 4$ b $x = 10$ c $x = 15$ d $x = 100$

3 Find the inputs x for the given outputs y for this function machine.

$x \rightarrow \boxed{\text{divide by 5}} \rightarrow y$

a $y = 3$ b $y = 6$ c $y = 10$ d $y = 20$

4 Find the inputs x for the given outputs y for this function machine.

$x \rightarrow \boxed{\text{multiply by 2}} \rightarrow \boxed{\text{subtract 10}} \rightarrow y$

a $y = 4$ b $y = 2$ c $y = 10$ d $y = 90$

TASK 2: Coordinates

Did you know that...?

The idea of coordinates on a grid was invented in 1637 by the French mathematicians **Rene Descartes** and **Pierre de Fermat**. But Fermat did not publish his discovery so Descartes got all the credit.

Descartes was born in 1596. His father was a judge but his mother died when he was one year old. He studied to be a lawyer but became a soldier instead.

Rectangular coordinates are sometimes called **Cartesian coordinates**, after Descartes. A region of the Moon, the landing place of Apollo 16, is also named after him.

The Descartes landing site on the Moon during the Apollo 16 mission

Points to remember

⊙ A coordinate pair is an ordered pair of numbers (x, y).

⊙ The x-coordinate is along the horizontal x-axis and the y-coordinate is up the vertical y-axis.

You will need squared paper, pencil and ruler.

1. Write the coordinates of the points A to H marked on the grid below.

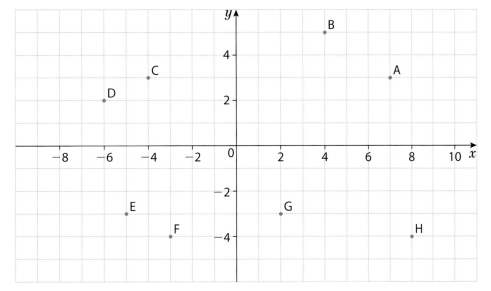

(2) You will need to draw and label a coordinate grid to answer this question.

ABCD is a square. Points A $(-1, 0)$, B $(3, 4)$ and C $(7, 0)$ are three of its vertices. What are the coordinates of the fourth vertex D?

TASK 3: Straight-line graphs

Points to remember

⊙ The x-axis is the line $y = 0$; the y-axis is the line $x = 0$.

⊙ Lines parallel to the x-axis, cutting the y-axis at $(0, c)$, have the equation $y = c$.

⊙ Lines parallel to the y-axis, cutting the x-axis at $(c, 0)$, have the equation $x = c$.

⊙ You can use coordinates of points on a straight-line graph to work out its equation.

(1) The vertices of a square PQRS are at P $(3, 3)$, Q $(3, -2)$, R $(-2, -2)$ and S $(-2, 3)$.
Write the equation of:

    a   PQ

    b   QR

    c   RS

    d   SP

    e   the horizontal line of symmetry of square PQRS

    f   the vertical line of symmetry of square PQRS

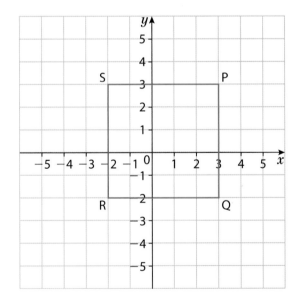

(2) Point T is $(2, -3)$.

    a   Write the equation of the horizontal line through T.

    b   Write the equation of the vertical line through T.

(3) Write the equation of the line through the points:

    a $(-4, 0)$ and $(4, 0)$ b $(-7, -8)$ and $(-7, 8)$

TASK 4: Plotting straight-line graphs

 Points to remember

- You can represent an equation like $y = 2x + 1$ as a straight-line graph.
- To draw the graph of $y = 2x + 1$, work out the coordinates of three points. Choose three values for x and calculate the values of y.
- There should be equal spaces between the numbers on the axes.
- Label the grid lines, not the spaces.
- Continue the line to the edge of the grid.

Example

Work out three pairs of coordinates (x, y) that lie on the graph of $y = 2x + 4$, then draw the graph.

x	0	1	2	Choose 3 values for x.
$y = 2x + 4$	4	6	8	Work out the values of y.

To draw the graph of $y = 2x + 4$, plot the coordinates (0, 4), (1, 6), (2, 8).
Join the points with a straight line. Extend the line to the edges of the grid.

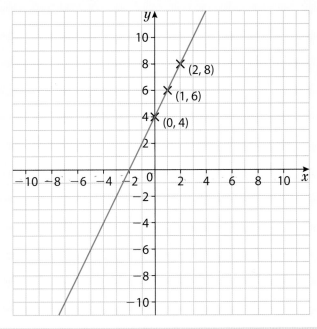

You will need squared paper.

① Draw graphs for these equations.

    a $y = x + 6$ **b** $y = x - 3$ **c** $y = 2x - 3$

TASK 5: Sequences

 Points to remember

⊙ The difference between consecutive terms of a sequence helps you to find the formula for the nth term.

Example 1

Find the nth term for the sequence:

3, 6, 9, 12, 15, …

The difference between consecutive terms is 3.
Each term in the sequence is 'a multiple of 3'.
The **1**st term is $3 \times$ **1**.
The **2**nd term is $3 \times$ **2**.
The nth term is $3 \times$ n or $3n$.

Example 2

Find the nth term for the sequence:

6, 11, 16, 21, 26, …

The difference between consecutive terms is 5.
Each term in this sequence is 'a multiple of 5, plus 1'.
The **1**st term is $5 \times$ **1** $+ 1$.
The **2**nd term is $5 \times$ **2** $+ 1$
The nth term is $5 \times$ n $+ 1$ or $5n + 1$

1. Find the formula for the nth term of each of these sequences.
    a 2, 4, 6, 8, …
    b 7, 12, 17, 22, …
    c 2, 5, 8, 11, …
    d 8, 15, 22, 29, …

2. Here are the formulae for the nth terms of some sequences.
    Write the 10th term and the 100th term of each sequence.
    a $n - 1$ b $n + 7$ c $7n - 3$ d $3n + 5$

Transformations

TASK 1: Line symmetry

> **Points to remember**
> - A shape has **line symmetry** when it can be folded so that one part of the shape fits exactly on top of the other part.
> - The fold line is the **line of symmetry**.

You will need squared paper.

1. How many lines of symmetry does each shape have?

   a trapezium   b square   c arrowhead   d pentagon

   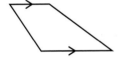  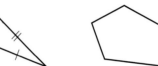

2. Copy each of these shapes on squared paper.
   Colour more squares to make a pattern that is symmetrical about the mirror line.

   a
   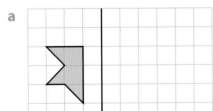

   b
   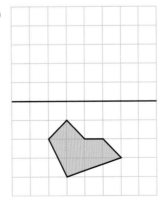

3. a Which of these numerals has one line of symmetry?

   0   1   2   3   4   5   6   7   8   9

   b Which of the numerals have two lines of symmetry?

TASK 2: Reflections

> ## ⦿ Points to remember
>
> ⊙ When an object is reflected in a mirror line, the image is the same size and shape as the object.
>
> ⊙ Corresponding points of the object and image are the same perpendicular distance from the mirror line.

You will need squared paper.

① Nick has drawn the reflection of the object in the mirror line.

   Explain what is wrong with Nick's drawing. Draw the correct answer.

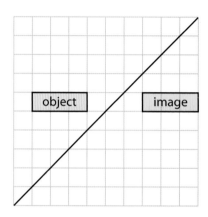

② Copy each of these shapes on squared paper. Reflect each one in the mirror line.

a
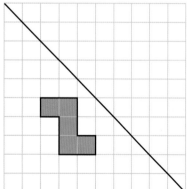

b
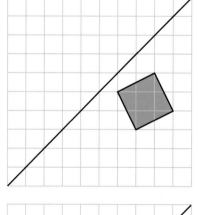

c
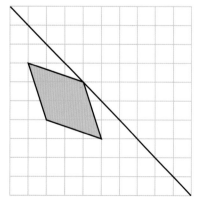

d
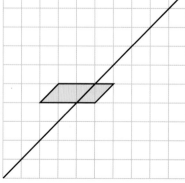

TASK 3: Rotation symmetry

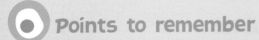
You will need squared paper.

1 What is the order of rotation symmetry?

a

b

c

d

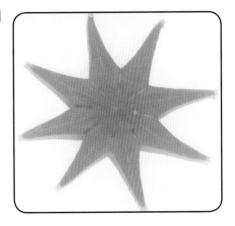

2 Which of these letters have rotation symmetry of order 2?

A B C D E F G H I J K L M

N O P Q R S T U V W X Y Z

3 This cross is made of 10 right-angled triangles.

  a What is the order of rotation symmetry of the cross?

  b Copy the cross on squared paper.
  Add two more right-angled triangles to make a new shape with rotation symmetry of order 2.

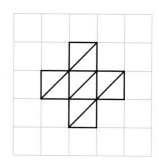

TASK 4: Rotations

Points to remember

- When an object is rotated:
  - every point of the object turns through the same angle in the same direction;
  - the image is the same size and shape as the object.
- The point about which a shape is rotated is the centre of rotation.

You will need **G3.3 Resource sheet 4.2**.

1 Answer the questions on **G3.3 Resource sheet 4.2**.

TASK 5: Translations

- When an object is translated:
  – every point of the object moves the same distance in the same direction;
  – the image is the same size and shape as the object.
- Movement to the right or left, or parallel to the x-axis, is described before movement up or down, or parallel to the y-axis.

You will need squared paper.

1. Describe the translation that moves triangle A to:

   a triangle B

   b triangle C

   c triangle D

   d triangle E

   e triangle F

   f triangle G.

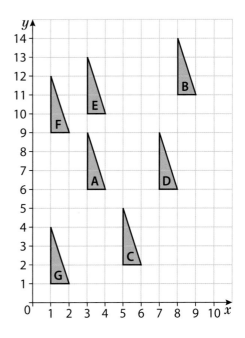

2. Using the diagram for question 1, write the translations for:

   a E to G

   b C to A

   c B to F

   d D to C

   e B to G.

Percentages, ratio and proportion

TASK 1: Equivalent fractions and percentages

⊙ **Points to remember**

- To change a decimal or a fraction to a percentage, multiply it by 100. For example, $\frac{3}{10}$ as a percentage is $\frac{3}{10} \times 100\% = 0.3 \times 100\% = 30\%$
- Use percentages to compare proportions.

120 people were asked to vote for their three favourite sports.

1. Three quarters of the people voted for football. What percentage voted for football?

2. How many people voted for football?

3. 36 of the people voted for swimming. What fraction of them voted for swimming?

4. What percentage of them voted for swimming?

5. 30 of the people voted for tennis. What percentage voted for tennis?

6. 20% of the people voted for athletics. How many people voted for athletics?

7. 35% of the people voted for basketball. How many people voted for basketball?

8. 6 people voted for table tennis. What percentage of the people voted for table tennis?

9. One eighth of the people voted for cycling. How many people voted for cycling?

10. What percentage of the people voted for cycling?

TASK 2: Finding percentages, including discounts

Points to remember

- Use informal methods to find percentages such as 10%, 5% and 15%, 50%, 25% and 75%.

- A quick way to find 20% is to find 10% by dividing by 10, then multiply this by 2 to find 20%. You can find 30%, 40%, … in a similar way.

- If there is no quick way, first find 1%, then multiply by the value of the percentage.

1. An electrical store has a sale.

Work these out using the most efficient method.

Video game £24	SALE PRICE one quarter off

a How much is the reduction?
b What is the sale price?

DVD player £75	SALE PRICE 25% off

c How much is the price reduced by?
d What is the sale price?

iPod £125	SALE PRICE 45% off

e What is the reduction?
f What is the sale price?

TV £275	SALE PRICE 8% discount

g How much is the discount?
h What is the sale price?

Laptop £635	SALE PRICE half price

i How much is the price reduced by?
j What is the sale price?

Colour printer £369	SALE PRICE $33\frac{1}{3}$% off

k What is the discount?
l What is the sale price?

TASK 3: Dividing a quantity in a given ratio

Points to remember

⊙ To divide a quantity into two parts in the ratio $a : b$:
  - first divide the quantity into $a + b$ equal units;
  - then put a units in one part, and b units in the other part.

Example
Divide £160 into two parts the ratio 3 : 5.

There are $3 + 5 = 8$ equal units. One unit is £160 ÷ 8 = £20.
So 3 units are £20 × 3 = £60, and 5 units are £20 × 5 = £100.

1. Divide £120 in each of these ratios.

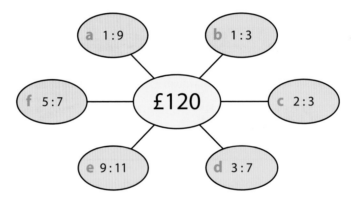

a 1 : 9
b 1 : 3
f 5 : 7
£120
c 2 : 3
e 9 : 11
d 3 : 7

2. Use your ruler to draw a line XY 78 mm long.
   Mark a point P so that XP to PY is in the ratio 4 : 9.
   Write the lengths of XP and PY in millimetres on your line.

3. a The ratio of male to female students at a college is 2 : 3.
     There are 1000 students at the college.
     How many male students are there?

   b There are 15 students altogether in a maths class.
     10 of them are female.
     What is the ratio of males to females in the class?

TASK 4: Direct proportion

Example

Tomatoes costs £4 for 1 kg. Emma buys some tomatoes for 80p.
How many grams of tomatoes does she buy?

cost (p)	tomatoes (g)
400	1000
80	?

÷ 5

Answer: Emma buys 1000 g ÷ 5 = 200 g of tomatoes.

1. Two tins of paint are enough paint to paint 8 square metres.
   How many tins of paint are needed to paint:

   a 32 square metres
   b 12 square metres?

2. 3 pencils cost 96p. Work out the cost of 5 of these pencils.

3. Four 1 litre tins of paint cost a total of £36.60.
   Work out the cost of seven of the 1 litre tins of paint.

4. This is a recipe for 10 pieces of nutty crunch.

   200 g of plain chocolate
   4 tablespoons of golden syrup
   50 g of margarine
   100 g of nuts

   Work out the amounts needed to make
   25 pieces of nutty crunch.

5. Kelly bought 4 cinema tickets for £17. Work out the cost of 9 of the tickets.

TASK 5: Conversion graphs

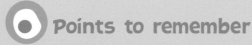

Points to remember

- Use a conversion graph to change from one unit to another.
- Conversion graphs are always straight lines.
- To draw a conversion graph, plot at least two points.
- It is not always possible to make an exact reading from a conversion graph.

① 5 miles is roughly the same as 8 kilometres.

   a How many kilometres is 15 miles?

   b How many miles is 32 kilometres?

   c How many miles is 20 kilometres?

② Look at this conversion graph for changing kilometres to miles.

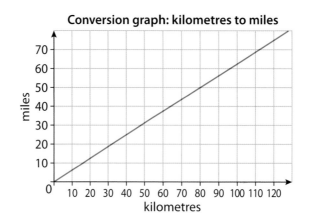

Estimate these distances in kilometres.

   a 30 miles   **b** 58 miles   **c** 69 miles

Estimate these distances in miles.

   d 30 km   **e** 75 km   **f** 108 km

Properties of shapes

TASK 1: Parallel and perpendicular lines

 Did you know that...?

Lines of latitude are the horizontal lines that run east-to-west on maps.

The **Equator** is the line of latitude that is halfway between the North Pole and the South Pole.

The **45th parallel** is the line of latitude halfway between the Equator and the North Pole.

Points to remember

- **Parallel lines** are always the same distance apart.
- Parallel lines never meet even if they are extended.
- **Perpendicular lines** meet or cross each other at right angles.
- On diagrams, parallel lines are marked with arrows, perpendicular lines are marked with a right angle.

1. You will need a ruler, set square and sharp pencil.
   Draw a pair of parallel lines.
   The perpendicular distance between them must be 6 centimetres.

2. Here are the names of seven special quadrilaterals:

   square   rectangle   parallelogram   rhombus   kite   arrowhead   trapezium

   Copy the table. Write the names of the quadrilaterals in the correct boxes:

Two pairs of parallel sides	One pair of parallel sides	No parallel sides

TASK 2: Properties of shapes 1

Points to remember

⊙ A **right-angled triangle** has one angle of 90°.

⊙ An **isosceles triangle** has two equal sides and two equal angles. It has one line of symmetry.

⊙ An **equilateral triangle** has three equal sides and three equal angles. It has three lines of symmetry and rotation symmetry of order 3.

⊙ A **quadrilateral** has four sides. Some special quadrilaterals are the square, rectangle, parallelogram, rhombus, kite, arrowhead, trapezium.

1 ABCD is a kite.

   a Which side is equal in length to AB?

   b Angle ABC is 123 degrees.
      What is the size of angle ADC?
      Give your reason.

   c How many lines of symmetry has a kite?

   d Does a kite have rotation symmetry?

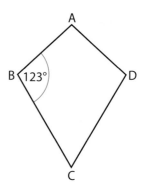

2 ABCD is a parallelogram.

   a Which angle is equal to angle ADC?

   b Angle BAD is 79 degrees.
      What is the size of angle DCB?
      State your reason.

   c Write down two pairs of parallel sides.

   d Which side is equal in length to DC?

   e How many lines of symmetry has a parallelogram?

   f What is the order of rotation symmetry of a parallelogram?

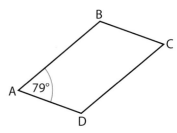

TASK 3: Properties of shapes 2

 Points to remember

⊙ The diagonals of a square, rhombus, kite and arrowhead cross each other at right angles.

⊙ The diagonals of a square, rectangle, parallelogram and rhombus cut each other in half.

⊙ The properties of shapes can be used to solve problems.

You will need squared paper. You may use tracing paper to help you if you wish.

① Triangle ABC is a right-angled triangle.
What shape do the triangle and its image make when:

   a triangle ABC is reflected in line AB?

   b triangle ABC is reflected in line AC?

   c triangle ABC is rotated 180° about the midpoint of AB?

   d triangle ABC is rotated 180° about the midpoint of BC?

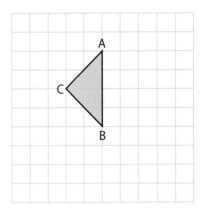

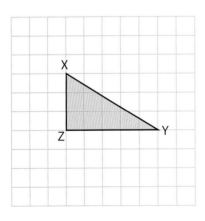

② Triangle XYZ is a right-angled triangle.
What shape do the triangle and its image make when:

   a triangle XYZ is reflected in line XY?

   b triangle XYZ is reflected in line YZ?

   c triangle XYZ is rotated 180° about the midpoint of XY?

   d triangle XYZ is rotated 180° about the midpoint of ZY?

TASK 4: Investigating shapes

◉ Points to remember

- ⊙ Triangles with special properties are an **equilateral triangle**, an **isosceles triangle** and **right-angled triangle**.
- ⊙ A triangle in which all three sides are different lengths is called a **scalene triangle**.
- ⊙ Scalene triangles can be **acute-angled** or **obtuse-angled**.
- ⊙ A quadrilateral has four sides. Some special quadrilaterals are the **square, rectangle, parallelogram, rhombus, kite, arrowhead** and **trapezium**.

You will need square dotty paper.

1) You can make three different sizes of squares on a 3 by 3 pinboard.

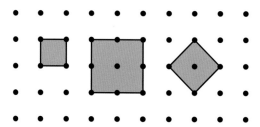

How many different sizes of squares can you find on a 4 by 4 pinboard?
Each square must have a pin at each corner.

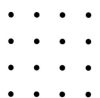

Make sure that you find all the different sizes and that you record your results.

2) Now try a 5 by 5 pinboard.

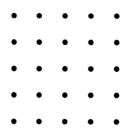

TASK 5: Angle sum of a triangle

Points to remember

⊙ Angles in a triangle add up to 180°.
   You can use this property to solve problems.
⊙ Never measure an angle that you are asked to calculate.

① Find the size of each angle marked with a letter.
   Give your reasons.

a
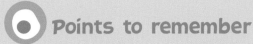
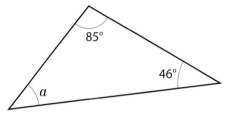

b
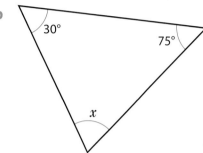

c
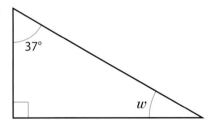

d
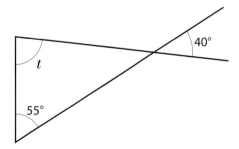

e
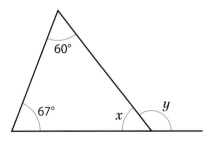

f
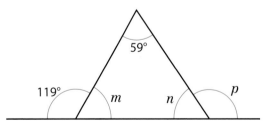

TASK 6: Solving problems

1. Find the size of each angle marked with a letter.
   Give your reasons.

   a
   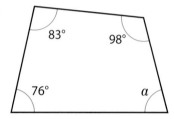

   b
   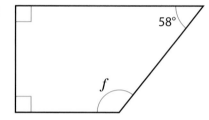

   c
   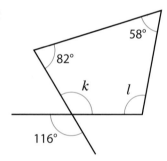

   d
   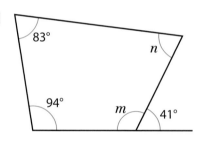

2. **a** The diagram shows an isosceles trapezium.
      Find the size of each angle marked with a letter.
      Give your reasons.

      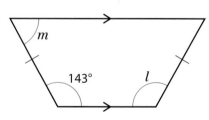

   b The diagram shows a kite.
      Find the size of each angle marked with a letter.
      Give your reasons.

      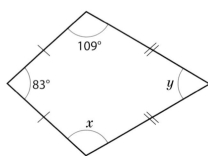

Enquiry 2

TASK 1: Collecting data

Points to remember

- When you plan a survey, it helps to think about the **data handling cycle.**

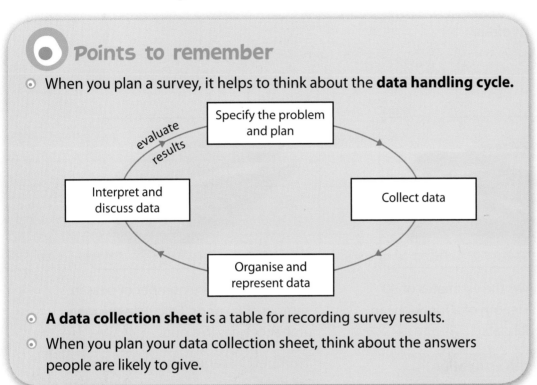

- **A data collection sheet** is a table for recording survey results.

- When you plan your data collection sheet, think about the answers people are likely to give.

1. Make a data collection sheet like this one but with 8 rows.

Person	Gender (male/female)	Age	Number of portions of fruit or vegetables eaten yesterday
1			
2			
3			
4			

Ask eight people if they will help you with your maths homework by taking part in a simple survey about the fruit and vegetables they eat.

Try to ask people of different ages.
Make sure that you have a mix of males and females.
Record their answers on the sheet.

TASK 2: Calculating statistics

 Points to remember

⊙ The **mean** is the sum of the numbers divided by the number of numbers.

⊙ The **median** is the middle number, or the mean of the middle two numbers, when you put all the numbers in order.

⊙ The **mode** or **modal class** is the number or group of numbers that occurs most often.

Example 1

The table shows the estimates of 30 people of the length of a runner bean. Find the modal class.

Length estimation	
Estimate (cm)	Frequency
21–25	3
26–30	7
31–35	5
36–40	12
41–45	3
46–50	1

The class that occurs most often is 36–40 cm, so this is the modal class.

Example 2

The table shows the number of peas in a sample of 30 pods. Calculate the mean number of peas in a pod.

Number of peas	Frequency	Peas × frequency
4	4	$4 \times 4 = 16$
5	3	$5 \times 3 = 15$
6	5	$6 \times 5 = 30$
7	5	$7 \times 5 = 35$
8	3	$8 \times 3 = 24$
TOTAL	20	120

Find the total number of peas by multiplying the number of peas by their frequencies and adding.

To get the mean, divide this total, 120, by the number of pods, 20.

$120 \div 20 = 6$

The mean number of peas in a pod is 6.

1 The tables show the number of words in a sentence for two newspapers.

Newspaper sentences (paper A)	
Number of words	Frequency
1–5	0
6–10	84
11–15	68
16–20	56
21–25	35
26–30	13
31–35	1

Newspaper sentences (paper B)	
Number of words	Frequency
1–10	7
11–20	10
21–30	7
31–40	4
41–50	0
51–60	1

Find the modal class for each paper.

2 30 pupils were asked about their eating habits.
The results are shown in the table.

Number of portions per day	Frequency			
	Fruit	Veg	Sweets	Crisps
0	5	3	5	2
1	2	8	8	8
2	12	11	7	8
3	10	4	6	6
4	3	0	0	3
5	0	2	0	3
6	0	2	3	0
7	0	0	1	0

a How many of the pupils ate no portions of vegetables in a day?

b What was the total number of portions of fruit eaten by the pupils?

c Calculate the mean number of portions of fruit, vegetables, sweets and crisps eaten in a day.

TASK 3: Using statistics

Points to remember

⊙ Use the range and a measure of average to compare two sets of data.

1   This bar chart shows the mean temperature in Washington DC, USA.

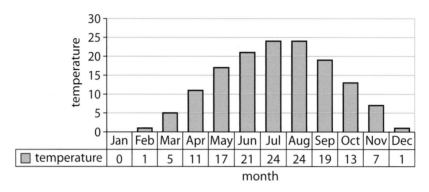

temperature	Jan	Feb	Mar	Apr	May	Jun	Jul	Aug	Sep	Oct	Nov	Dec
	0	1	5	11	17	21	24	24	19	13	7	1

month

This bar chart shows the mean temperature in Sydney, Australia.

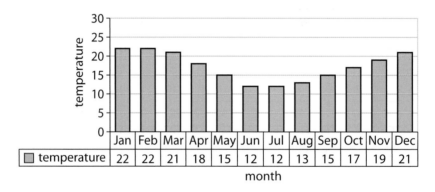

temperature	Jan	Feb	Mar	Apr	May	Jun	Jul	Aug	Sep	Oct	Nov	Dec
	22	22	21	18	15	12	12	13	15	17	19	21

month

a   What is the range for the temperature in each city?

b   Which city is hotter in April?

c   Why do the two graphs have different shapes?

d   Work out the mean temperature for each city.

e   Write a few sentences comparing the temperatures in the two cities.

TASK 4: Representing data

1 Annie has asked some pupils what they had in school for lunch.
Some of her results are:

Year group	Did you have lunch in school?	Own lunch or cafeteria?	Chocolate?	Crisps?	Fruit or veg?
7	Y	Own	Y	Y	N
7	Y	Own	N	Y	Y
8	N				
9	Y	Cafeteria	N	Y	N
7	Y	Cafeteria	Y	N	Y

a What percentage of pupils in Annie's survey had lunch in school?

b How many pupils had chocolate with their lunch?

c How many pupils had crisps or chocolate or both?

d Write two possible questions that Annie could answer with her survey.

2 Mark and John have made a table of their cricket scores for their last 10 matches:

Game	1	2	3	4	5	6	7	8	9	10
Mark	12	20	35	33	22	19	45	0	37	44
John	7	12	15	19	46	24	51	54	19	20

a Work out the range and mean of Mark's cricket scores.

b Work out the range and mean of John's cricket scores.

c Which do you think is the better player, Mark or John? Why?

③ The pie chart shows the different forms of transport pupils use to travel to school.

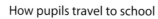

How pupils travel to school

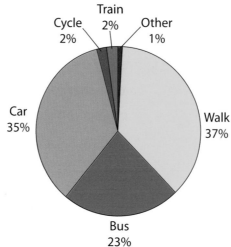

a Which is the most common form of transport?

b Which three methods of transport account for almost all travel to school?

c Write two sentences to say what the pie chart shows.

TASK 5: Interpreting and discussing data

⦿ **Points to remember**

- ⊙ Choose charts and graphs that help to answer the question.
- ⊙ Make sure that you know why you chose that chart or graph.
- ⊙ Write down what each chart, diagram or calculation shows you about the data.
- ⊙ Check that you have answered the original question.

Look at the information in the six boxes on the next page.
They are from two reports.
The labels on the horizontal axis of the graphs have been accidentally cut off.

① List the lettered boxes for each report in the order that you would write the report.

② Write a conclusion for each report.

A Table

Hours per day	Girls	Boys
None	3	6
Less than 1	12	15
1 up to 2	18	24
2 up to 3	21	17
3 up to 4	20	19
4 up to 5	14	6
5 up to 6	8	4
Over 6	4	9

B Question

Do boys prefer to play team sports more than girls do?

C Question

Do girls watch more television than boys?

D Graph

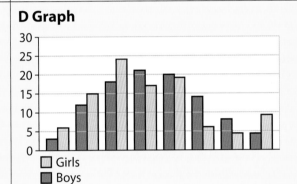

E Graph

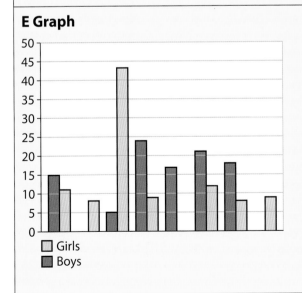

F Table

Sport	Percentage of girls	Percentage of boys
Trampolining	15	11
Rugby	0	8
Football	5	43
Swimming	24	9
Netball	17	0
Hockey	21	12
Badminton	18	8
Cricket	0	9

Constructions

TASK 1: Drawing line segments and parallel lines

Points to remember

- **Perpendicular lines** meet or cross each other at right angles.
- **Parallel lines** are always the same distance apart; the perpendicular distance between them is always the same.
- Parallel lines do not need to be the same length.
- Leave construction lines on your drawings.

You will need a ruler, set square and sharp pencil.

1. Use a ruler to measure these line segments.

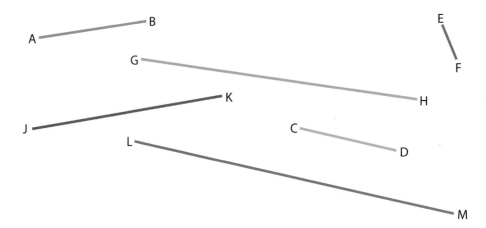

2. Use your ruler to draw a line segment 11 cm long.
   Label the line AB.
   On the line AB, mark a point C that is 3 cm from A.
   At C, use your set square to draw a line CD perpendicular to line AB.

   Now draw a line parallel to CD, at a distance of 5 cm from CD. Label this line EF.
   Leave your construction lines on your drawing.

TASK 2: Constructing shapes with right angles

You will need a ruler, protractor and sharp pencil.

1. Make an accurate drawing of a rectangle with length 8 cm and width 6 cm. Measure the length of one of its diagonals.

2. Make an accurate drawing of a square with a perimeter of 12 cm. Measure the length of one of its diagonals.

TASK 3: Acute, obtuse and reflex angles

Example   Draw an angle of 300°.

First work out the acute angle: 360 − 300 = 60°.

Draw a straight line OA.

Position the protractor with its centre at O so that line OA is under the base line of the protractor.

Measuring from the base line over OA, mark 60° at point B.
Join OB.

The required angle of 300° is the reflex angle AOB.

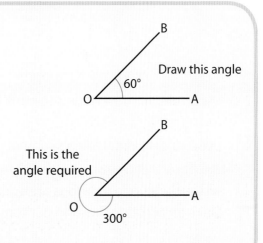

You will need a ruler, protractor and sharp pencil.

(1) Measure these angles.

(2) Use a ruler to draw a line segment DE, 7 cm long. Now draw angle DEF = 200°.

(3) Use a ruler to draw a line segment JK, 5 cm long. Now draw angle LJK = 330°.

(4) All four sides of a rhombus are equal.
     Make an accurate drawing of rhombus WXYZ.

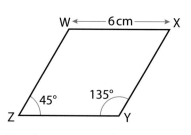

Not drawn accurately

TASK 4: Constructing triangles

Points to remember

- **Congruent triangles** have the same angles and are the same size.

- All triangles that have the same side-angle-side (SAS) measurements are congruent.

Two sides and the included angle (SAS)

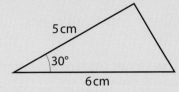

- All triangles that have the same angle-side-angle (ASA) measurements are congruent.

Two angles and the included side (ASA)

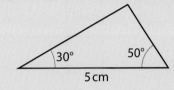

You will need a ruler, protractor and sharp pencil.

1. Construct triangle ABC, with AB = 7 cm, angle ABC = 50° and BC = 5 cm.

   a Measure AC.

   b Measure angle BAC.

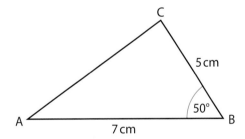

2. Construct triangle LMN, with angle LMN = 45°, MN = 9 cm and angle MNL = 45°.

   a Measure LM.

   b Measure LN.

   c Measure angle MLN.

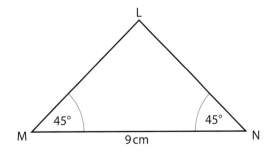

TASK 5: Nets of 3D shapes

> ## ⦿ Point to remember
> ⦿ A **net** is a 2D surface that can be folded into a 3D shape or solid.

You need a ruler, set square and sharp pencil.

① The diagram shows a net that folds up to make a cube.

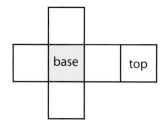

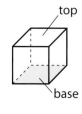

A sketch of another net for a cube is on the right.

Make an accurate drawing of the net using a ruler and set square.
Make each side 3.5 cm long.

Label where the top will be when the cube is folded up.

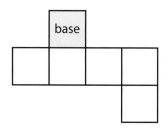

② The sketch shows the net of a triangular prism. Each outside edge is labelled with a letter. Tabs have been added to some edges so that the net can be folded up and glued to make the prism.

  a Which edge will tab 1 be glued to?

  b Which edge will tab 2 be glued to?

  c Which edge will tab 3 be glued to?

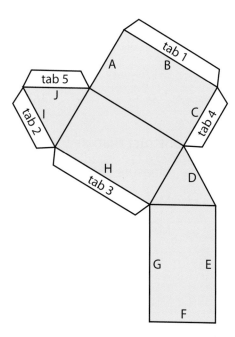

TASK 6: Properties of 3D shapes

Points to remember

⊙ A **net** is a 2D surface that can be folded into a 3D shape or solid.
⊙ A **prism** is a 3D shape or solid that has the same cross-section throughout its length.
⊙ A **pyramid** is a 3D shape that has a polygon for its base. Its other faces are triangles that meet at a common vertex.

You will need a ruler, protractor and sharp pencil.

(1) Here is a net of a 3D shape.
All its edges are 4 cm long.
When the net is folded up, what 3D shape will it make?
Choose from this list:
cube
square-based pyramid
tetrahedron
cuboid
triangular-based pyramid
octahedron

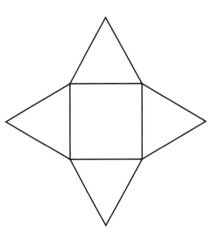

(2) Make an accurate drawing of the net in question 1.

(3) The picture shows a regular tetrahedron.

Each of its four faces is an equilateral triangle.
Each of its six edges is 5 cm long.

Use your ruler and protractor to construct the net for this tetrahedron.

TASK 1: Working with expressions

> ### ⦿ Points to remember
>
> ⊙ Each part of an algebraic expression is a **term** of the expression, e.g. for the expression $3n + 5$ the terms are $3n$ and 5.
>
> ⊙ **Like terms** have the same combination of letters. For example, $2b$ and $-5b$ and b are all like terms.
>
> ⊙ You can simplify expressions by collecting like terms.
>
> ⊙ You can evaluate expressions by substituting values for the letters.

1. A bunch of daffodils costs d pence.
   A bunch of tulips costs t pence.

   a What is the cost of 5 bunches of daffodils?

   b What is the total cost of 3 bunches of daffodils and 2 bunches of tulips?

   c What is the difference in price in pence between a bunch of daffodils and a bunch of tulips?

   d How much change in pence do you get from £5 for 2 bunches of daffodils and a bunch of tulips?

2. Work out the value of each expression when $p = 10$, $q = 4$ and $r = 3$.

   a $p + q + r$

   b $p + q - r$

   c $p - q - r$

   d $p - 2q - 3r$

   e $2p - 2q - 2r$

   f $2p - 3q - 3r - 1$

3. Multiply out the brackets and simplify the expression.

   a $3(n + 7) + 2(n + 1)$

   b $6(a + 1) + 3(a - 2)$

   c $5(x - y) + 2(x + y)$

   f $4(p + q) - 5q$

TASK 2: Functions and equations

Points to remember

⊙ The equation $y = 5x - 4$ can be written as a function like this:

$x \rightarrow$ | multiply by 5 | $\rightarrow$ | subtract 4 | $\rightarrow y$

⊙ Given a value for x, work through the function to find the value of y.

⊙ Given a value for y, work through the inverse function to find the value of x.

⊙ The inverse of addition is subtraction.
The inverse of subtraction is addition.
The inverse of multiplication is division.
The inverse of division is multiplication.

① Write these equations as functions of x.

   a $y = x + 15$ b $y = 7x + 4$ c $y = 11x - 2$ d $y = \dfrac{x}{9} + 10$

② Write these functions as equations in x and y.

   a $x \rightarrow$ | add 14 | $\rightarrow y$ b $x \rightarrow$ | multiply by 8 | $\rightarrow y$

   c $x \rightarrow$ | divide by 3 | $\rightarrow y$ d $x \rightarrow$ | multiply by 2 | $\rightarrow$ | add 3 | $\rightarrow y$

   e $x \rightarrow$ | multiply by 7 | $\rightarrow$ | subtract 3 | $\rightarrow y$ f $x \rightarrow$ | divide by 2 | $\rightarrow$ | add 7 | $\rightarrow y$

③ Write the inverse functions.

   a $x \rightarrow$ | add 100 | $\rightarrow y$ b $x \rightarrow$ | subtract 15 | $\rightarrow y$

   c $x \rightarrow$ | multiply by 16 | $\rightarrow y$ d $x \rightarrow$ | divide by 9 | $\rightarrow y$

   e $x \rightarrow$ | multiply by 3 | $\rightarrow$ | add 8 | $\rightarrow y$ f $x \rightarrow$ | multiply by 7 | $\rightarrow$ | subtract 1 | $\rightarrow y$

TASK 3: Solving equations

 Did you know that...?

Amelie Noether was a German mathematician who did ground-breaking work in algebra. Her nickname was Emmy, so she is usually referred to as **Emmy Noether**.

Emmy was born in 1882 and died at the age of 53. She has been described as 'the best woman mathematician of the 19th century'.

This old photograph of her was taken just before she first went to university.

Amelie Noether

 Points to remember

⊙ The left-hand side of an equation must always balance the right-hand side.

⊙ Whatever you do to the left-hand side of an equation, you must do to the right-hand side.

Example   Solve $x + 3 = 17$.

To solve the equation first work out the inverse function.

$$x + 3 = 17 \qquad x \to \boxed{+3} \to 17$$

subtract 3 $\underline{x = 14}$ $14 \leftarrow \boxed{-3} \leftarrow 17$

① Find the value of x.

a $x + 25 = 72$ b $x - 21 = 55$

c $9 + x = 26$ d $17 + x = 33$

e $4x = 12$ f $11x = 99$

g $x - 1.5 = 3.5$ h $\frac{x}{5} = 3$

TASK 4: Square and triangular numbers

 Did you know that...?

The sequence of **square numbers** is $1, 4, 9, 16, 25, 36, \ldots, n^2, \ldots$

The sequence of **triangular numbers** is $1, 3, 6, 10, 15, 21, \ldots, \frac{1}{2}n(n + 1), \ldots$

Every **square number** is the **sum of two triangular numbers.**

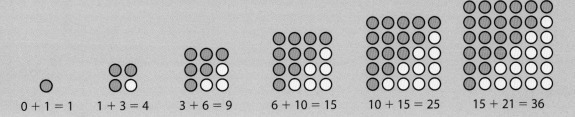

$0 + 1 = 1 \qquad 1 + 3 = 4 \qquad 3 + 6 = 9 \qquad 6 + 10 = 15 \qquad 10 + 15 = 25 \qquad 15 + 21 = 36$

 Points to remember

⊙ The **nth term** of a sequence is the term in the nth position.

⊙ If you know the nth term, you can generate the sequence by substituting $n = 1, n = 2, n = 3$, and so on.

⊙ You can find any term by substituting its position into the nth term. For example, if the nth term is $3n + 6$, the 25th term is $3 \times 25 + 6 = 81$.

1 Write the first five terms of the sequences with these nth terms.

 a $8n$ b $n + 1$

 c $4n - 3$ d $5n + 9$

 e $10n - 3$ f $3n + 7$

 g $\frac{n}{2}$

2 Work out the 50th term of the sequences with these nth terms.

 a $8n$ b $n + 11$

 c $3n - 12$ d $2n + 5$

 e $5n - 7$

3 The nth term of a sequence is $\frac{1}{2}n(n + 1)$.

 a Write the first 10 terms of the sequence.

 b What are the numbers in this sequence called?

TASK 5: More sequences from patterns

1. Here is a sequence of numbers

   3,   5,   7,   9,   …

   Work out the 20th term of this sequence.
   Explain how you worked out your answer.

2. Jason investigated these patterns of pink and blue dots.

| Pattern 1 | Pattern 2 | Pattern 3 |

Number of blue dots	Number of pink dots
1	10
2	17
3	24
4	31
5	38

a How many pink dots are needed for 6 blue dots?

b How many pink dots are needed for 10 blue dots?

c How many pink dots are needed for n blue dots?

TASK 6: Interpreting real-life graphs 1

Points to remember

- A **linear graph** is one that consists of straight lines.
- Read the labels and axes before reading any values from the graph.
- Think about the context of the graph.

1. Jack walks from home to his friend Jo's house.
   He spends some time there.
   Jack then walks to the shops.
   After spending some time at the shops he walks back home.

   This graph records Jack's journey to and from the shops.

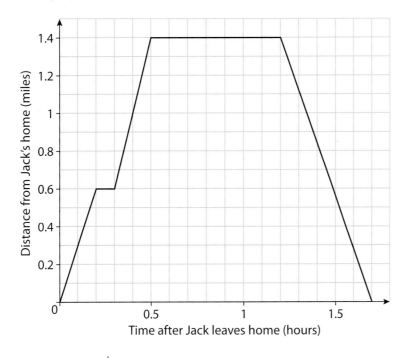

   a Jack leaves home at 10:30 am. At what time does he arrive at Jo's house?

   b How long does Jack spend at Jo's house?

   c How long does it take Jack to walk from Jo's house to the shops?

   d How far from Jack's house are the shops?

   e How long does Jack spend at the shops?

   f How long does it take Jack to walk from the shops back home?

   g What is Jack's average walking speed on his way home from the shops?

TASK 7: Interpreting real-life graphs 2

1 This graph shows the conversion between degrees Fahrenheit (°F) and degrees Celsius (°C).

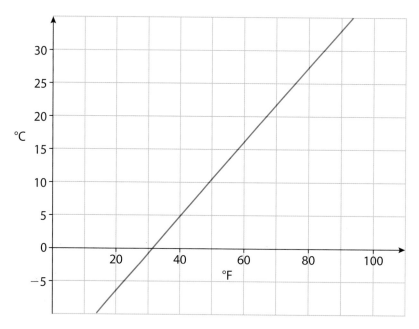

a Use the graph to change 60 degrees Fahrenheit to degrees Celsius.

b Use the graph to change 10 degrees Celsius to degrees Fahrenheit.

c The temperature in London on 15 July was 30°C.
Estimate what this is in degrees Fahrenheit.

d When Rupert was ill his body temperature rose to 100°F.
Estimate what this is in degrees Celsius.

e The temperature in Glasgow on 1 January was −4°C.
Estimate this in degrees Fahrenheit.

f The difference in temperature between two towns is 12 degrees Celsius.
Use the graph to estimate this difference in degrees Fahrenheit.

g Water freezes at 0 degrees Celsius.
Estimate this temperature in degrees Fahrenheit.

TASK 8: Using ICT to draw graphs

1 This is the graph of the equation $y = x$.

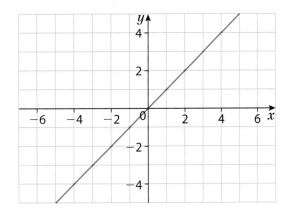

    a At what point does this graph intersect the x-axis?

    b At what point does this graph intersect the y-axis?

2 **a** Sketch the graph of $y = x$.

    b On the same axes sketch the graphs of $y = x + 1$ and $y = x + 2$.

3 **a** Sketch the graph of $y = x$.

    b On the same axes sketch the graphs of $y = 2x$ and $y = 3x$.

Probability 2

TASK 1: Equally likely outcomes

> ### ◉ Points to remember
>
> ⊙ **Probability** is measured on a scale from 0 (impossible) to 1 (certain).
>
> | impossible | unlikely | even chance | likely | certain |
> |---|---|---|---|---|
>
> 0 $\frac{1}{2}$ 1
>
> ⊙ Probabilities can be written as fractions, decimals or percentages.
> ⊙ **An event** can have different **outcomes**.
> ⊙ **Equally likely outcomes** have the same chance of happening.
> ⊙ For equally likely outcomes, the **probability** of an event is:
>
> $$\frac{\text{number of favourable outcomes for the event}}{\text{total number of possible outcomes}}$$

Example

In a pack of 52 playing cards there are 13 cards of each suit: spades, clubs, hearts and diamonds.

One card is taken at random from a pack of cards.

a What is the probability of taking a spade?

There are 13 spades out of 52, so the probability of taking a spade is $\frac{13}{52}$ or $\frac{1}{4}$.

b What is the probability of taking a red card (a diamond or a heart)?

There are 26 red cards so it is $\frac{26}{52}$ or $\frac{1}{2}$.

1   There are 26 letters in the alphabet. The vowels are A, E, I, O and U. One letter from the is picked at random from the alphabet.

    a   What is the probability that it is a vowel?

    b   What is the probability that it is not a vowel?

    c   What is the probability that it is the letter T?

2   The letters from the word CARROT are placed in a bag .
    One letter is taken out at random.
    What is the probability of taking out:

    a   the letter C?   b   the letter R?

    c   the letter M?   d   the letter A or the letter O?

3   John rolls a fair 12-sided dice numbered from 1 to 12.

    What is the probability of rolling these numbers?

    a   6   b   an odd number

    c   zero   d   a number greater than 6

    e   a prime number   f   a multiple of 7

TASK 2: Experimental probability

Points to remember

⊙ The **experimental probability** is:

$$\frac{\text{number of successful trials}}{\text{total number of trials}}$$

1   You will need a coin.

    Copy this tally chart.

Outcome	Tally	Frequency
Head		
Tail		

    Throw your coin 50 times.
    Record your results in the chart.

    Use your chart to answer these questions.

2   What is the experimental probability of throwing:

    a   a tail?   b   a head?

3   What is the theoretical probability of throwing:

    a   a tail?   b   a head?

TASK 3: Comparing probabilities

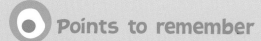
For each of the four statements below, say whether it is **true** or **false**.
Explain each answer.

(1) There are 3 red counters, 2 green counters and 4 yellow counters in a bag.

The probability of picking a red counter at random is $\frac{1}{3}$.

(2) It is harder to throw a 6 than a 1 with a fair 1 to 6 dice.

(3) When United plays Rovers, United can win, lose or draw.
The probability that they will win is $\frac{1}{3}$.

(4) Tomorrow it will either snow or not snow.
The probability of it snowing is 0.5.

Solving number problems

TASK 1: Word problems

 Points to remember

To solve word problems:

- ⊙ identify key information;
- ⊙ decide what operation is needed in each step;
- ⊙ change measurements to the same unit;
- ⊙ estimate the answer, then do the calculation;
- ⊙ check that the answer makes sense;
- ⊙ write the answer clearly.

Solve these problems **without using a calculator**. Show all your working.

1. Simon and Lucy go to the garden centre.

   a Lucy has £50.
      She buys 3 flowerpots and a spade.
      How much money does she have left?

   b Seeds are 58p for a packet.
      Simon has £9 to spend on seeds.
      What is the greatest number of packets he can buy?

2. This is the cost to visit a science museum.

   a One morning 14 adults and 28 children visited a
      science museum. How much did they pay altogether?

   | Adults | £8.50 |
   | Children | £4.50 |

   b Guide books cost 23p each.
      The museum takes £9.43 from selling guide books to a coach party.
      How many people bought a guide book?

3. One soft drink and a box of popcorn together cost £2.21.
   Two soft drinks and a box of popcorn together costs £3.53.
   What does a box of popcorn cost?

TASK 2: Working with fractions

Points to remember

- To simplify a fraction, divide the numerator and the denominator by the same number.

  Example: $\dfrac{18}{30} = \dfrac{18 \div 6}{30 \div 6} = \dfrac{3}{5}$

- To change a fraction into an equivalent fraction, multiply the numerator and the denominator by the same number.

  Example: $\dfrac{5}{8} = \dfrac{5 \times 125}{8 \times 125} = \dfrac{625}{1000}$

- To compare the size of fractions, change them to equivalent fractions with the same denominator.

- To work out what fraction one number is of another, divide the first number by the second number and then cancel.

Example

What fraction is 36 of 48?

$\dfrac{36}{48} = \dfrac{3}{4}$ (cancelling by 12), so 36 is $\dfrac{3}{4}$ of 48.

1. Copy and complete these sets of equivalent fractions.

   a $\dfrac{8}{18} = \dfrac{\square}{9} = \dfrac{\square}{27}$

   b $\dfrac{75}{125} = \dfrac{\square}{5} = \dfrac{\square}{100}$

   c $\dfrac{24}{81} = \dfrac{3}{\square} = \dfrac{\square}{4}$

   d $\dfrac{30}{50} = \dfrac{15}{\square} = \dfrac{\square}{5} = \dfrac{6}{\square}$

   e $\dfrac{49}{98} = \dfrac{7}{\square} = \dfrac{1}{\square} = \dfrac{\square}{12}$

   f $\dfrac{74}{111} = \dfrac{2}{\square} = \dfrac{\square}{117}$

2. In each pair of fractions, which fraction is larger?

   a $\dfrac{3}{5}$ or $\dfrac{2}{3}$

   b $\dfrac{7}{9}$ or $\dfrac{3}{4}$

   c $\dfrac{5}{16}$ or $\dfrac{9}{24}$

3. For each pair of fractions, what fraction lies halfway between them?

   a $\dfrac{3}{5}$ and $\dfrac{4}{7}$

   b $\dfrac{1}{3}$ and $\dfrac{3}{5}$

   c $\dfrac{3}{11}$ and $\dfrac{5}{9}$

TASK 3: Fractions, decimals and percentages

Points to remember

⊙ To change a fraction to a decimal, divide the numerator by the denominator, e.g. with a calculator.

Example: $\frac{13}{20} = 13 \div 20 = 0.65$

① You may find it helpful to make some squares from scrap paper.
Write 1, 2, 4, 5, 6, 8 and 9 on the squares.

$$\boxed{1} \quad \boxed{2} \quad \boxed{4} \quad \boxed{5} \quad \boxed{6} \quad \boxed{8} \quad \boxed{9}$$

In each problem, use each of four digits.
Put one digit in each box.
Make a fraction and its decimal equivalent.

a Use each of the digits **1**, **5**, **8** and **9**.

$$\frac{\square}{\square} = \square.\square$$

b Use each of the digits **1**, **4**, **5** and **6**.

$$\frac{\square}{\square} = \square.\square$$

c Use each of the digits **1**, **5**, **6** and **9**.

$$\frac{\square}{\square} = \square.\square$$

d Use each of the digits **2**, **4**, **5** and **9**.

$$\frac{\square}{\square} = \square.\square$$

② Find a fraction that is bigger than one quarter and less than one third.
You may **use a calculator**.

TASK 4: Comparing proportions

1. Cheeseburgers contain 30% fat.
   Beefburgers contain 25% fat.
   Which of these contains more fat?
   A a 220 g cheeseburger
   B a 270 g beefburger

2. Mrs Adams and Mrs Baker both sell fruit on their market stalls.
   The pie charts show their sales of fruit last Saturday.

   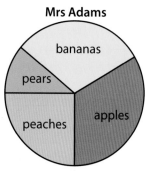

   Mrs Adams

   Total: £1000

   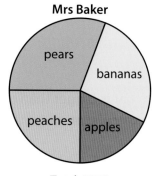

   Mrs Baker

   Total: £800

   a Estimate how much Mrs Adams took from selling pears.

   b Estimate how much Mrs Baker took from selling apples.

   c Who took more from selling peaches?

3. Jyoti scored 18 out of 20 in a maths test and 22 out of 25 in an English test.
   In which subject did she have a higher score?

TASK 5: Ratio and proportion problems

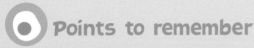

Points to remember

⊙ You can simplify ratios like fractions by dividing each side by the same number, so 5 : 10 is equivalent to 1 : 2.

This sequence of patterns is made from blue and green counters.

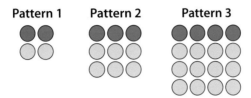

1. What is the ratio of blue to green counters for each pattern?
   Write your answer in its simplest form.

2. What will be the ratio of blue to green counters for the 4th pattern in the sequence?

4. Write down the ratio of blue to green counters for the 20th pattern.

4. Copy and complete this table.

Pattern number	1	2	3	4	5	6
Total number of counters						

5. Write down the total number of counters for the 20th pattern.

6. Use the ratio of blue to green counters for the 20th pattern.
   How many blue counters are there in the 20th pattern? How many green counters?

Revision unit 1

TASK 1: Whole number and decimal calculations

> ### ◉ Points to remember
>
> ⊙ Try as many questions as possible. The easier questions are not always at the beginning.
>
> ⊙ Use jottings to help with mental calculations.
>
> ⊙ If you have a choice, consider whether it is best to use a mental, written or calculator method.
>
> ⊙ Show your working, including in calculator questions. You may get a mark for your method.
>
> ⊙ Check that answers are sensible and about the right size.

You may **use a calculator** to answer these questions.

1995 level 5

 a Robert and Gwen must put 63 tins of food into a lift.
Each tin weighs 840 g.

Work out the total weight of the 63 tins in grams.

b In the lift there is a sign.
It shows the greatest load that the lift can carry safely.

Look at the total weight of the 63 tins, which you worked out in part **a**.
Is it safe to carry the 63 tins together in the lift?
Give a reason for your answer.

> **Greatest Load**
> **50 kg**

 The height of a tin is 14 cm.
The height of a cupboard is 1.24 m.

How many layers of tins can be kept in the cupboard?

TASK 2: Fractions, decimals and percentages

 Points to remember

- There are quick ways to find 50%, 25%, 75%, 10%, 5%, 15%, and multiples of 10%.
- If there is no obvious quick way to find a percentage, find 1%, then multiply by the value of the percentage.
- If there is a choice, decide whether to use a written or calculator method.
- Always include any units in your answers.

Example

Find 47% of £85.
1% of £85 is £85 ÷ 100 = £0.85 or 85p.
47% of £85 is 1% × 47, or £0.85 × 47 = £39.95.

You may **use a calculator** for questions 2 and 3.

(1) *2000 level 5*

The table shows some percentages of amounts of money.

	£10	£30	£45
5%	50p	£1.50	£2.25
10%	£1	£3	£4.50

Copy and complete the calculations below. Use the table to help you.

a   15% of £30 = £...

b   £6.75 = 15% of £...

c   £3.50 = ...% of £10

d   25p = 5% of £...

(2) *2000 level 5*

Copy and complete these calculations.

a   8% of £26.50 =

b $12\frac{1}{2}$ % of £98 =

(3) *Year 7 Optional Test level 5*

The area of the Earth's surface is 510 million km².
Only 29% of this is land.

Calculate how many million km² of land there are on the Earth's surface.

TASK 3: Expressions and equations

Points to remember

- $3n + 5$ is an algebraic **expression**. An expression has at least one letter.
- Each part of an expression is a **term** of the expression, e.g. the terms of the expression $3n + 5$ are $3n$ and 5.
- **Like terms** have the same combination of letters, e.g. $2x$ and $5x$ and x are all like terms.
- You can simplify an expression by collecting like terms.
- The left hand side of an equation must always balance the right hand side.

---

1 *2004 level 4*

Solve these equations.

a $a + 12 = 24$ b $b - 12 = 24$

2 Simplify:

a $7 + 2x + 3x$ b $y + 7 + 2y + 10$

3 *2002 level 5*

A teacher has a large pile of cards.
An expression for the total number of cards is $6n + 8$.

a The teacher puts the cards in two piles.
The number of cards in the first pile is $2n + 3$.
Write an expression to show the number of cards in the second pile.

first pile   second pile

b The teacher puts all the cards together.
Then he uses them to make two equal piles.
Write an expression to show the number of cards in one of the piles.

TASK 4: Charts, graphs and simple statistics

Points to remember

⊙ The **mode**, **median** and **mean** are different ways of finding the average of a set of numbers.

⊙ The **range** shows the spread of the numbers.

⊙ Graphs and charts are useful for showing features and making comparisons.

⊙ When you answer questions about graphs and charts, look at the title, the labels and scales on the axes, and any key.

⊙ When you compare two graphs, look for similarities and differences.

You will need a copy of **R3.1 Resource sheet 4.1**.

Complete questions 1 and 2 on the resource sheet.

(3) *2003 Progress Test level 4*

This question is about pupils in class 7Y.
The graph shows how many of these pupils were at school each day.

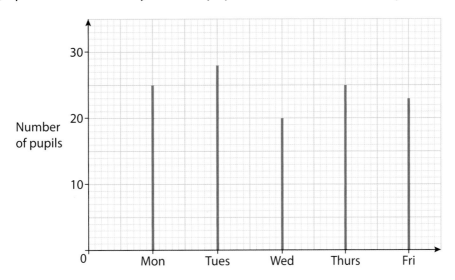

a On which days were only 25 pupils at school?

b On Tuesday all the pupils in class 7Y were at school.
How many of these pupils were not at school on Wednesday?

TASK 5: Probability

Points to remember

- Probabilities are usually written as fractions or decimals but are sometimes written as percentages.
- For equally likely outcomes, the **theoretical probability** of an event is:

$$\frac{\text{number of successful outcomes}}{\text{total number of possible outcomes}}$$

- The **experimental probability** of an event is:

$$\frac{\text{number of successful trials}}{\text{total number of trials}}$$

Example

The numbers on a 10-sided fair dice are 1, 2, 3, 4, 5, 6, 7, 8, 9, 10.

Sam wants to throw an even number.
The **theoretical probability** of throwing
an even number is 5 out of 10.
You can write this as the fraction $\frac{5}{10}$,
the decimal 0.5, or the percentage 50%.
Sam does an experiment.
He rolls the 10-sided dice 50 times.
He rolls an even number 30 times.

The **experimental probability** of rolling an even number is 30 out of 50.
You can write this as the fraction $\frac{30}{50}$, the decimal 0.6 or the percentage 60%.

---

(1) *2003 Progress Test level 4*

a Gill puts four counters in a bag.
Three counters are black. One counter is white.

Gill is going to take a counter out of the bag without looking.
What is the probability that the counter will be white?

b Sam puts 20 counters in a different bag.
She is going to take a counter out of the bag without looking.
The probability that the counter will be red is $\frac{1}{2}$.
How many red counters are in her bag?

2 *2005 level 5*

a Aidan puts two white counters and one black counter in a bag.

He is going to take one counter without looking.
What is the probability that the counter will be black?

b Aidan puts the counter back in the bag and then puts more black counters in the bag.
He is going to take one counter without looking.

The probability that the counter will be black is now $\frac{2}{3}$.
How many more black counters did Aidan put in the bag?

3 *2000 level 5*

A school has a new canteen.
A special person will be chosen to perform the opening ceremony.
The names of all the pupils, all the teachers and all the canteen staff are put into a box.

One name is taken out at random. A pupil says:

> There are only three choices.
> It could be a pupil, a teacher or one of the canteen staff.
> The probability of it being a pupil is $\frac{1}{3}$.

The pupil is wrong.
Explain why.

Revision unit 2

TASK 1: Solving word problems

> ### ⦿ Points to remember
>
> **Stage 1: Make sense of the problem**
> - ⦿ Read a word problem carefully and identify key information.
> - ⦿ Decide what you need to find out.
>
> **Stage 2: Calculate the answer**
> - ⦿ Write down the calculation that you need to do.
> - ⦿ Change units to the same unit if necessary.
> - ⦿ Choose efficient calculation methods.
> - ⦿ Show your working, including in calculator questions. You may get a mark for your method.
>
> **Stage 3: Check and explain the answer**
> - ⦿ Write down your answer to the problem. Include any units.
> - ⦿ Look back at the original problem and check that the answer is sensible and about the right size.
> - ⦿ Decide what to record to 'explain your answer'.

(1) *2006 level 4*

A bottle contains 250 ml of cough mixture.

One adult and one child need to take cough mixture 4 times a day every day for 5 days.

Will there be enough cough mixture in the bottle?

Explain your answer.

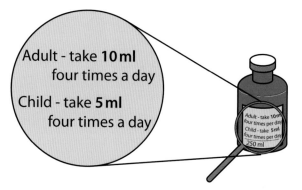

Adult - take **10 ml** four times a day

Child - take **5 ml** four times a day

(2)   a   A shop sells DVDs for £12.50 each.
         What is the cost of 16 DVDs?

      b   The shop sells CDs.
         Each CD costs £7.99.
         What is the cost of 4 CDs?

      c   How many CDs at £7.99 each can
         you buy with £65?

      d   The shop also sells CDs in packs of three.
         A pack costs £19.99.
         How many packs can you buy with £65?

      e   What is the greatest number of CDs you can buy with £76?
         You can buy some packs at £14.99 and some single CDs at £7.99.

(3)   *2004 level 5*

      You can buy a new calculator for £1.25.
      In 1979 the same type of calculator cost
      22 times as much as it costs now.

      How much did the same type of calculator cost in 1979?
      Show your working.

TASK 2: Ratio

Points to remember

⊙ To simplify a ratio, divide each side by the same number.
  For example, 5 : 10 is equivalent to 1 : 2.

⊙ To divide a quantity into two parts in the ratio 2 : 7, divide it into
  2 + 7 = 9 equal shares. Put 2 shares in one part, and 7 shares in the
  other part.

Example 1

Divide 6 kg of carrots in the ratio 7 : 3.

There are $7 + 3 = 10$ equal units.
For one unit, calculate 6 kg ÷ 10 = 0.6 kg.
For seven units, calculate 0.6 kg × 7 = 4.2 kg.
For three units, calculate 0.6 kg × 3 = 1.8 kg.

So 6 kg divided in the ratio 7 : 3 is 4.2 kg : 1.8 kg.

Example 2

A line segment is divided in the ratio 2 : 3.
The shorter part of the line is 12 cm long.
What is the length of the longer part?

12 cm represents two units of the line.
For one unit, calculate 12 cm ÷ 2 = 6 cm.
For three units, calculate 6 cm × 3 = 18 cm.

So the longer part of the line is 18 cm.

---

① *2005 level 5*

Work out the number of boys and girls
in each class below.

a In class 8M, there are 27 pupils.
   There are twice as many boys as girls.
   How many boys are there? How many girls?

b In class 8K, there are 28 pupils.
   There are two more boys than girls.
   How many boys are there? How many girls?

c In class 8T, there are 8 boys.
   The ratio of boys to girls is 1 : 2.
   How many girls are there?

② A number line starts at 2 and finishes at 22.
   The arrow divides the line in the ratio 2 : 3.
   What number is the arrow pointing to?

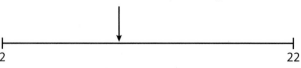

   Show your working.

TASK 3: Sequences, functions and graphs

Points to remember

⊙ A sequence of numbers follows a rule.

⊙ You can work out the next number in a sequence if you know the term-to-term rule.

⊙ You can work out any term in a sequence if you know the formula for the nth term.

⊙ A coordinate point is represented by an ordered pair of numbers (x, y).

⊙ Always look at the labels on a graph before you read any values.

⊙ Work out carefully the values of intervals on the scales on the axes.

 2001 level 5

You will need a copy of **R3.2 Resource sheet 3.4** to do this question.

a   You pay £2.40 each time you go swimming.
Copy and complete the table.

Number of swims	0	10	20	30
Total cost (£)	0	24		

b   Show this information by drawing a graph on the resource sheet.
Join the points with a straight line.

c   A different way of paying is to pay a yearly fee of £22.
Then you pay £1.40 each time you go swimming.
Copy and complete this table.

Number of swims	0	10	20	30
Total cost (£)	22	36		

d   Now show this information on the same graph on the resource sheet.
Join the points with a straight line.

e   For how many swims does the graph show that the cost is the same for both ways of paying?

Here is a sequence of shapes made with grey and white tiles.

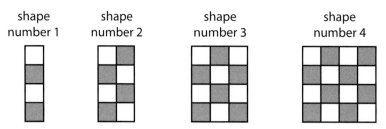

| shape number 1 | shape number 2 | shape number 3 | shape number 4 |

> The number of grey tiles = 2 × the shape number
> The number of white tiles = 2 × the shape number

a Altogether, how many tiles will be in shape number 5?

b Altogether, how many tiles will be in shape number 15?

c Copy and complete this sentence:

The total number of tiles = … × the shape number

TASK 4: Area and perimeter

⊙ Points to remember

⊙ **Perimeter** is the distance around the edge of a shape.

⊙ **Area** is a measure of the surface covered by a shape.

⊙ Area of a rectangle = length × width.

⊙ To find the surface area of a 3D shape, add the areas of all its faces.

⊙ A **net** is a 2D surface that can be folded into a 3D shape or solid.

(1) *2004 level 4*

The diagram shows some shapes on a 10 by 6 square grid.

a Which two shapes have the same area as shape A?

b Which two shapes have the same perimeter as shape A?

c How many of shape C would you need to cover a 10 by 6 square grid?

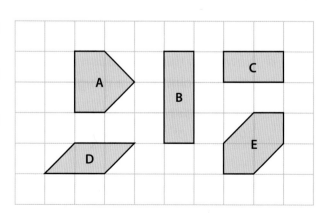

2 *2001 level 5*

  a Write down the letter of any rectangles below that have an area of 12 cm².

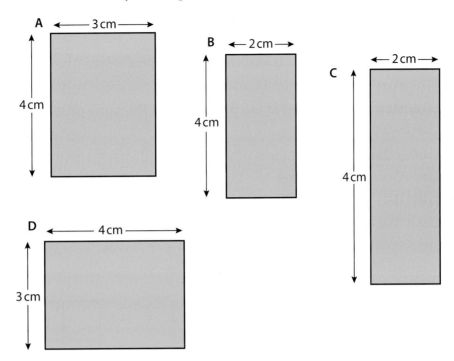

  b A square has an area of 100 cm². What is its perimeter?
  Show your working.

3 *1999 level 5*

The diagram shows a rectangle 18 cm long and 14 cm wide.
It has been split into four smaller rectangles.

Make a sketch of the diagram.
Write the area of each small rectangle on the diagram.
One has been done for you.

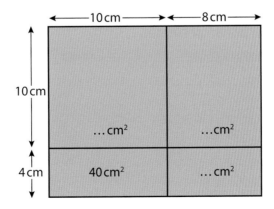

What is the area of the whole rectangle? Show your working.

TASK 5: Symmetry and transformations

> ## ⦿ Points to remember
>
> ⊙ In a **reflection**, **rotation** or **translation**, the original shape (the object) and the image are the same size and shape.
>
> ⊙ In a **translation**, each point of the object moves the same distance in the same direction.
>
> ⊙ In a **reflection**, matching points of the object and image are the same distance from the mirror line.
>
> ⊙ In a **rotation**, each point of the object turns about the centre of rotation through the same angle in the same direction.

(1) *2006 level 4*

Copy this square grid.

Shade two more squares so that the grid has two lines of symmetry.

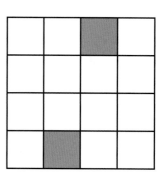

(2) *2004 level 5*

a A pupil measured the angles in a triangle.
She said: 'The angles are 30°, 60° and 100°.'

Could she be correct? Write **Yes** or **No**.
Explain your answer.

b This diagram is not drawn accurately.

Calculate the size of angle *m*.
Show your working.

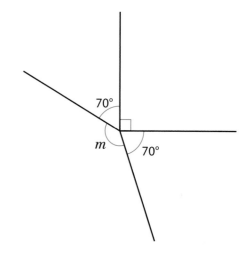

3 *2003 level 5*

Look at the diagram.

Triangle ABD is the reflection of triangle ABC in the line AB.

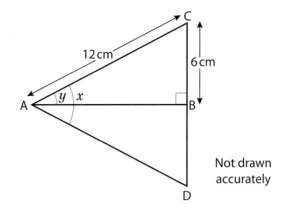

Not drawn accurately

Copy and complete the sentences below.

Fill in the gaps below to explain how to find angle x.

The length of AC is 12 cm.

The length of AD is … cm.

The length of CD is … cm.

ACD is an equilateral triangle because ....

So angle y is …° because ....

So angle x is …° because ....